throat
sprockets

throat
sprockets

tim lucas

FOURTH ESTATE • *London*

First published in Great Britain in 1995 by
Fourth Estate Limited
6 Salem Road
London W2 4BU

Copyright © 1994 by Tim Lucas

The right of Tim Lucas to be identified as the author of this work
has been asserted by him in accordance with the
Copyright, Designs and Patents Act 1988

A catalogue record for this book is available from the British Library

ISBN 1-85702-318-8

Printed in Great Britain by Clays Ltd, St. Ives plc

To anyone who ever gave me a chance—
Especially you, PERK

ACKNOWLEDGMENTS

Throat Sprockets is the fulfillment of an unfinished graphic novel. Only three chapters were completed: "Throat Sprockets" and "Transylvania, Mon Amour," illustrated by Mike Hoffman, respectively appeared in *Taboo* #1 (1987) and *Taboo* #3 (1989); "The Disaster Area," illustrated by David Lloyd, still awaits print. I'm grateful to Stephen R. Bissette, the publisher/editor of *Taboo*, for his constant support and encouragement of this project throughout its early stages of development, arrested and otherwise.

Additional thanks to Bill Kelley for one or two anecdotes that found their way into the final mix, and to Jeanne Cavelos, Lori Perkins, and the late Cathy Mahar for the motivating force of their enthusiasm.

And my profoundest thanks to Robert Uth for introducing me to the incantatory value of black coffee, the magic of sentimental drives, and the adventure of fiction.

T.L.

1

The cinema comes to life with dark—like Dracula.

David Thomson
America in the Dark

THROAT SPROCKETS

HE FIRST TIME I SAW *THROAT SPROCKETS* WAS AT THE OLD EROS THE-
ater; it's long gone, but I visit it often in memory. I can still see
the CALL THEATER FOR TITLES advisory on its weather-beaten marquee . . . hear the squeak of its seats . . . picture its mildewed
screen, billowing gently from a broken backstage window . . .
smell the brown crayon soup dispensed by the coffee machine in
its lobby. All of these things are forever linked in my senses to the
adventure they portended.

The Eros was a civic embarrassment located in the heart of
downtown Friendship, Ohio, three blocks south of the Sutton
Building, where I worked. I liked spending my lunch hours in its
darkened seclusion. The redhead in the ticket booth never complained if, over the spangled rim of her cat's-eye glasses, she
caught sight of a carryout lunch under my arm. The usher, her
ancient confederate, was never more than ten paces away, wearing a suit that had seen its best days during the Eisenhower ad-
ministration, talcum powder and Brylcreem embalming the bath
he had taken a week before. He was always quick to alert me
when the movie had already started.

There was never an afternoon rush at the Eros, no competition for seats, so—as an advertising man—I took pleasure in examining the one-sheet posters framed along the lobby walls. The usher had torn my tickets often and felt sufficiently free, when he saw me fire up a cigarette in his little museum, to reminisce. As I studied the poster for *I Beg Your Hard-on* and its acrylic portrait of Andrea Bazin's ecstatic mouth, he told me that I was standing in the second oldest still-standing movie palace in the state of Ohio. The theater's antiquity was more than evident from the lobby, where unwashed marmoreal columns supported a long-neglected mezzanine. The upstairs had been roped off, I heard, since the day it was discovered that someone had taken a dump amid the balcony seating, wiping himself on one of the red crushed velvet draperies. I patiently listened to the usher's stock of Eros stories, none for the first time: about its early years as the Pica Theater, how it had played host in the thirties to famous stage acts such as W. C. Fields and Joe Yule ("That's Mickey Rooney to you, before MGM went and changed his name"), and his peculiar boast that Tyrone Power had once worked there as an usher.

I liked to take a long draw on my cigarette, tilt my head back, and blow smoke into the dizzying heights of the lobby's bronze dome, an inverted eye glowering gigantically down on a Chinese red carpet stained with spilled coffee and muddy shoes, dusted with bronze chips and peelings. As I approached the auditorium doors, pausing only long enough to admire the poster for Debbie W. Griffith's *Rolling Doughnut*, I heard my tour guide lament—to me, to himself, to Tyrone's ghost, or anyone else who might listen—"This place used to be real classy. . . . Now it's all pickles and beavers."

I should explain that adult movies—X movies, Triple X, whatever you want to call them—have never particularly aroused me. On the contrary, I found myself drawn to them because of my disenchantment with mainstream films; I was fed up and growing weak on a steady diet of movies made by money and interested only in attracting more money. American films had become an art form with the agent as auteur; their lack of serious adult concerns was enforced by an outmoded and unrealistic ratings system that refused free expression to works of original or unpopular thought. I was driven by my attitude to the hard-core circuit, where the odds of being satisfied by a mature story line were slightly more in my favor—even if those odds were one in a thousand, at least the chance *existed*. Adult films also had a peculiar knack for capturing the listlessness I found at the core of real life, better than so-called "legitimate" films. By the time you reach thirty, as I had, you're either just learning to appreciate the anesthetic value of escapism or growing sick of the vapors. I was so much of the latter persuasion that I had completely lost all interest in actors, in the craft of performance. I could no longer stomach the annual broadcast of the Academy Awards. Once you've seen a representative sampling of adult films, you begin to see that the gulf between the acting abilities of the cast of a $40 million summer blockbuster and a $75,000 skin flick, filmed on the sly over a weekend in a barricaded Holiday Inn suite, isn't so vast. In fact, if they were made a few years apart, the casts might even be the same—at least here and there. You'd be surprised.

I stumbled through a darkness alleviated only by the grace of a dim exit sign and found a seat at my preferred vantage—aisle seat, down front, no closer than the seventh row—just as the screen brightened, broadcasting light throughout the theater's spacious, once luxuriant interior. Two, possibly three women were cavorting in the projected light, prompting a drunken patron in the back to groan in half-feigned agony, "Where do they *get* these broads to do that? Jesus, they're better lookin' than my *wife!*"

He was shushed by a loudly amused, slur-voiced companion. "You wanna get ush thrown out?"

True to the warnings of Tyrone's torchbearer, the movie had already started. It was the typical hard-core translation of a recent blockbuster; you know the kind: *Beverly Hills Cock, Sperms of Endearment, Dirtysomething, Edward Penishands. Mad* magazine for brain-dead grown-ups. This time Twatgirl was hot on the trail of her archnemesis, the Diddler. Commissioner Hardon was flashing the Twat Signal over the skies of Bottom City. Bottom City was, in fact, a barely adequate matte painting, its skyline incorporating a number of imposing, dildoesque skyscrapers, a sight that had long since ceased to amuse its matinee audience. After a few minutes of this farce even the corporate logo on my Hardee's carryout bag suggested a rude double entendre.

I was passively amused by the film, obviously the tuition scheme of some clever but misguided university film students, but its erotic content felt as distant to me as my own sophomore years. Its overfamiliar images of hairy male paws wrestling with female flesh, lifting it and spreading it and turning it over, revisiting its swells and tucks again and again in redundant positions, coupled with the filmmakers' leering disrespect for it, left me limp with indifference. My eyes occasionally wandered away from the screen during the film's brighter sequences, which shed light into the ancient baroque stylings of the theater's untended ceiling, where dancing devils and Art Nouveau cherubs watched faceless, interchangeable women milking men with the same joyful expressions that had been carved into their faces to appreciate the pratfalls of Buster Keaton and the high-rise hijinks of Harold Lloyd.

After devouring my lunch and refusing a fellow patron the loan of a napkin, I settled back and let my eyes roam freely over abstract images of racially mottled motion, my mind freed by the omniscience of seeing strangers engaged in intimate acts to drift wherever it wished. Though I was free to imagine anything and explore that fantasy with total authority, I found my thoughts drifting back to a certain one-sheet poster I had glimpsed in the lobby. The poster had depicted a woman's throat—slender, its translucent airbrushed skin stretched taut in a craning posture—framed from the bow of her clavicle to the heartlike cleft of her chin. In a macabre touch the outer edges of her neck had been perforated with film sprockets, each tiny hole leaking thin, gleaming rivulets of blood. The title on the poster was *Throat Sprockets* and it had been framed under a banner that read NOW PLAYING. I had barely glanced at the poster while smoking my cigarette, but I was able to remember vividly every detail, every color and brushstroke. There was no artist's signature, but whoever he was, he certainly understood a great deal about advertising. In retrospect, maybe he understood a great deal about me.

The first feature ended with a predictable orgy in Twatgirl's Wet Cave, all of her masked sidekicks and paunchy commissioners vasectomized, with that telltale dimple behind their testes, all of them shooting blanks. The film was followed by a couple of trailers—so explicit, how could the films themselves deliver more? —and the start of the next feature. I glanced at my watch and decided that I could probably invest another twenty minutes or so in the cause of my cinematic education.

The cofeature began inauspiciously, to say the least. There was no date of copyright but the color had turned red and the print was badly worn. I recognized the music at once, an instrumental library track that evoked a sense of danger and intrigue which had been used in countless nudies since the heyday of James Bond. The plain, almost hand-printed card announcing LOTUS FILMS PRESENTS was followed by no immediate flesh images to keep the raincoat crowd riveted to their seats; further credits had been spliced out as an irrelevance. Whatever the reason, my lingering sense of insult helped me to appreciate this burgled pang for what it was, because this adamant refusal of names—tantamount to a refusal to lie—had touched me in a far more personal way than the usual crawl of squirrelly pseudonyms. The splice—as conspicuous as a sidewalk fault—intimated to me that I wouldn't be told or shown or asked to share in anything, within the confines of this new experience, that wasn't one hundred percent true. I simmered as the story began to take shape.

Story?

There *was* no story.

The film was narrated by a dry, reedy, female voice, but I wasn't sure whether these poetical asides, with their liquid, fluctuating tenses, were spoken by anyone in particular in its revolving cast of characters. The men and women in *Throat Sprockets* appeared only long enough to create false expectations within the viewer. Certain actors stood out because they were given names in the midst of numerous anonymities—then they disappeared, dismissed from the scheme as some other, equally misleading newcomer stepped to the fore. Other characters appeared only in detail, as human mosaics—an inclining nape, a pensive glance, a parched mouth, a voluminous hairstyle—mysterious glimpses that left the viewer thirsting for more information. No character's face was ever shown in full, a mise-en-scène that enabled the film's participants to remain perfectly anonymous, and therefore perfectly truthful. *Throat Sprockets* had been filmed MOS ("*mit* out sound"—as the German fathers of cinema coined it), and though it was quite possible that the actors were speaking English, their mouths were typically averted when they spoke, which made it impossible to tell whether the dialogue had been dubbed, post-synchronized, or invented from whole cloth. After its initial danger theme the music segued gradually into a soothing and seductive calm, not unlike the ambient Muzak that carpets one's aural senses in shopping malls. There were no telling exteriors, no glimpses of famous landmarks to betray the locations where the film had been shot. The locations on view were almost exclusively dermal. Scenes pivoted on probing close-ups of questioning smiles, neck muscles being relaxed with massage, plush red thirsty lips being pursed and licked. But the point of these accumulating images never quite pronounced itself, instead continually receding into a flirtatious haze.

The clothes of the participants were never shed. The script's avoidance of sexual intercourse suggested that it, too, was an irrelevance. Each scene moved inexorably toward a point of tension that was suggestive and inviting, then pushed on without explanation or fulfillment to its next implicit diagram. From the promising concupiscence of two mouths whispering to one another in confidence, each moving closer to the other—cut: to the next oral conflict, gestating in the shapes between the shadows cast by two perfect strangers. The film radiated an aura that was palpably erotic, yet superficially innocent; it could have played on television. Everything was suggested; everything was actual *except* what was happening.

I had always been a "breast man" (as they used to say), preferring bouncy Eurosex farces to the swarthy, Brooklyn-made crotch operas that regularly played at the Eros. Nevertheless, I found myself humored, intrigued, and—finally—*responding* to *Throat Sprockets* and the quiet insistence of its offbeat, central obsession. By the time the first couple of reels had unspooled, the film's true fixation had become abundantly clear.

The director had a thing for *women's throats.*

Once this fact was fully disclosed, you were suddenly in the grip of something stronger and more decisive than your own level of interest. Whenever the film's oddly framed, fetishistic digressions sobered to the point of permitting its performers a few lines to speak—or when the cinematographer dollied back from the motions of a swallow to permit a less concentrated view of a woman's entire body—you found yourself zooming in, forging your own private close-ups, powerless to take in that broader view. The throats—you couldn't take your eyes off them. At least, *I* couldn't.

To be perfectly honest I had never given much thought to women's throats before, had never really appreciated how varied they were in their allure. *Throat Sprockets* showed them all: some throats were smooth, veiling the plunging mechanisms of talking and weeping and singing and swallowing in velourian swathes and points of pigment; others were pellucid, like a scarf held up to sunlight; and I learned how certain habits like typing, reading, knitting, even simple shyness—any routine that involved looking down for long periods of time—tended to buckle the skin of the throat and form attractive creases; how a strategically placed mole or birthmark made a world of difference to that textured canvas. . . .

• • •

It was indeed a world of difference that I discovered upon leaving the Eros that summer afternoon. I wasn't able to hang around for the end of the movie—business beckoned from the dial of my watch—but having been denied the emotional outlet that the final reel must have provided, I was haunted for the rest of the day by the anxiety of this film's accumulated images. Without learning how the rising tensions of those coaxing images were ultimately resolved, I stepped outside into a world where, to my delight, nearly every woman within eyeshot seemed to exhibit her sex openly, without fear, cover, or shame.

The three blocks back to my office at Sutton Perry & Ingersoll were a revelation. I was no longer satisfied to stop at the surfaces of things; I found myself responding instead to the hidden implications underlying the surfaces of life. I must have looked foolish, walking and laughing to myself as my eyes darted from fellow pedestrians to the magazine covers in news kiosks to advertisements on the sides of passing buses, and finding in every bared throat a form of racy pornography that only I could see. The provocation of my sightings ran deep, but none touched me more pointedly than the major question posed by the film itself: *What was a film like* Throat Sprockets *doing, playing the hard-core circuit?*

• • •

Most of the women at SPI were wearing their hair up, more in concession to fashion than comfort. I sat in my cubicle at my art table, my concentration on a public service announcement storyboard waning in the heat of other preoccupations. Time and time again I looked up from my pretense at industry to study a beam of sunlight emblazoning the auburn wisps of hair on Colleen Sangster's nape. She must have felt my eyes boring into her, because she turned abruptly to face me, our eyes locking for a split second before I could resume a feigned interest in what I was drawing.

Colleen waited to strike up a conversation until Barry Castleman left his adjacent cubicle. She was relatively new to SPI, and though we knew one another by sight, we had never actually spoken before.

"Zat me?"

I wasn't sure what she meant, but her question made me turn to my sketch pad. Sure enough, the lines I'd drawn in my distraction could indeed be interpreted as a cameo portrait of her. More precisely, it was a deflected cameo, a mosaic much in the style of the female fragments encountered in *Throat Sprockets*.

"Maybe," I allowed.

She lowered her voice. "I'm flattered," she said, calling me by name, "really, but y'know, if Mr. Ingersoll catches you passing the time like that . . ." Her words extended a wing of complicity between us; a veil to flirtation.

"He wouldn't say anything," I told her. "You see, I know things. Things that could keep me here. Indefinitely."

Her eyes glazed, greedy for gossip; I liked them. "You've got dirt on the Old Man?"

"Better than that," I told her. "I have dirt on his son."

"Dish on! What dirt have you got on his son?"

"I just happen to know—"

"Hm-hm?"

"—that he draws dirty pictures on company time—of girls—with their heads held just—like—so."

"Bullshitter! You're not his son."

"No, but I'm *like* his son."

"And I wouldn't exactly call that"—she pointed at the sketch—"dirt." Her face was so pretty that I was taken aback by the ugliness of her hands. Her fingers were stubs, their nails polished dark red, the color of clotted blood.

"No," I supposed, "but it's *like* dirt."

The following pause was less pregnant than contraceptive.

She asked me again, her eyes trained—a man can tell—just past the drawing, to my wedding band, as if trying to determine its value to me. "C'mon now, fess up. Is that really me?"

"Not really."

"Well, you know, that's *all right* . . ."

I took this opportunity, which found both of us poised much too soon on the edge of a precipice much too steep, to tell her I was married.

"Well, that's okay too. These days, they say married men aren't such a shot in the dark. . . ."

I guess we sort of left it at that.

· · ·

I've lost six close friends in the last eighteen months, Mr. Koppel. Two of them lovers. What our group is trying to do is address the fact that we gays are going to have to school ourselves in achieving new forms of eroticism. We must come to grips with the plain and simple fact that genital contact—for the moment, and possibly for the long haul—is simply out. Out, until further notice. . . .

That night, as the dialogue from an all-night news special conveyed bulletins of big-city urgency to our midwestern apartment, I surprised Paige with the best neck massage she'd ever had. It wasn't an unusual service for me to render—infrequently, she asked me to knead the stresses of a long, deskbound day from her shoulders—but to start without being asked, I knew, was irresistibly rare. It was a duty I tended to perform in a state of distraction ·bordering on absence, even when the television wasn't on.

During this stage of our marriage, massage had become a more regular evening ritual than lovemaking, and often decided better than we could with words whether or not love would be made. If she asked for a rub without any trace of exhaustion in her voice, I read this as a signal that she might be receptive; I would stand behind her, loosening her subterranean tensions with my thumbs, after which one of my hands would slip on its oiled palm down the front of her gown to collect the reward of a breast. This time, however, I found myself examining her neck in its pleasured tilts and swoons with my eyes as well as my hands, feeling as stimulated as if I were new not only to this custom but to Paige herself.

I lavished her with golden oil, lubricating the surface of her skin, translucing her neck and shoulders to my sense of touch. I was able to locate the knots of her discomfort at once and focused on the maladjustments of her higher vertebrae, until they adjourned under an equally stubborn pressure. With this release came a smoldering sigh, permission to advance. Without deliberation I instinctively veered off on an altogether different course. The oiled hands that traditionally dropped to plunder the front of her gown rose instead to either side of her neck, my eyes guiding them, burning in appreciation of its grace and shapeliness. After a respectful pause in which I did nothing but explore these parts of Paige I had always taken for granted, my fingers gently began to slip along the edges of her throat, stroking it with attentive delicacy, amplifying in my memory its every slope, every groove, its finery, folds, and flaws—until the possibilities dilated behind my closed eyes into a realm entirely their own. My thoughts raced. Paige's throat, I realized, was the tender juncture where her thoughts and feelings came together to form a common voice, a pleasantly husky voice that pleaded with me, *Whatever you're doing don't stop*, swathed in a pennytoss pelt of her parents' pooled cells, a map with highway arterials of blue and red. At one such intersection I found a spot in the crook of her neck where my touch triggered a delightful rash of gooseflesh. Paige clamped my fingers between her jaw and shoulder; the eyes she turned on me at that moment were aggressively, daringly sexual, in a way meant more to challenge than encourage.

"Don't you dare!" she urged. "Not there!"

"Not there?" I asked. "Then . . . *where?*"

I accepted the gift of my wife's body that night with inexplicable awkwardness; I behaved in her arms like a virgin given his first unschooled plunge into full-fledged, hair-grown sexual intercourse, unable to express my desire with any more ardent demonstration than a chaste, tight-lipped kiss. Afterward Paige brought me unexpectedly back from oblivion by tugging at my cheek, a playful smile animating her face. When I asked what she was trying to do, she said: *"Unmask you!"*

"What?"

"I've slept with the same man for twelve years. You didn't go after my boobs *once* tonight—you imposter!"

I found it impossible to sleep after she made that observation and thought a soak might help to relax me. I reclined in the bath, a wet washcloth matted to my face to block out the shine of the tiles and chrome and light. I chewed the sopping edge of the cloth in my mouth. In the dark behind the flannel I felt as if I were waiting for yet another curtain to come up. The temperature of my bath must have been 98.6 degrees—as warm as human blood—because I could feel the outline of my body vanish, as it cradled me, in surrender to the water. I woke an hour later, stifling because most of the flannel had crept inside my mouth, chewed into a ball.

You didn't go after my boobs once, you impostor.

I honestly don't remember that I ever did again.

• • •

Throat Sprockets played one more day at the Eros. I had hoped to get out of the office in time for the five o'clock showing, but Old Man Ingersoll ambled into my cubicle as I was reaching for my coat and reminisced to me about his dead partners until the picture was half over. As its companion feature was being screened, I loitered over a fettuccine dinner at Sarno's until shortly before the final showing.

The flame-haired cashier peered at me curiously as I bought my second ticket in as many days. That night, attendance at the Eros was much greater, evidently bolstered by people like myself who doubted they could live with themselves without knowing why a movie like *Throat Sprockets* had been booked into a hard-core theater. I felt a calming sense of requital as the houselights dimmed.

Seeing those early scenes from *Throat Sprockets* for the second time was like taking the second lesson toward a second language: remembering certain "phrases" from the previous screening made the new ones easier to grasp. I sat in the dark analyzing the film's roseate images, much as one replays the dialogue from old relationships one regrets and cannot explain. The persistence of clothed bodies, the constant attention to medium-close shots that framed the head and shoulders, these combined to intensify the film's subtly fetishistic bent—drawing my eye, unresistingly, along an invisible arrow to the throat always at the unspoken center of composition.

Eventually the film arrived at the point of its previous interruption. During the second half, as the throats of various young women—all of the same type—were openly admired by the attentive camera, a major character was introduced as audience surrogate. Only his hands were shown; two anonymous hands entering into frame to divest the women's throats of their scarves and beads and buttoned collars, engulfing the willowy models, one by one, in a proprietary caress until the camera extracted a "performance" from the unactable truth of an excitedly jogging jugular. As he stroked and caressed the visibly vital throb with one hand, the object of his attentions dressed his free hand in a white rubber glove, then the other. The face of the Glover, as he came to be known, was never revealed.

I was impatient, however, for *Throat Sprockets* to entrust me with the answer of how to fulfill the abstract desires that were taking shape within me. Scene after scene the film painted the viewer

into a series of intolerably erotic corners, each shunted aside—
mere seconds shy of culmination—by an irritating and tactless
splice, a gap that propelled one toward new scenes, new mosaics,
new throats, new questions. The splices increased, a cacophony
of ravished emulsion each time a new throat was bared. The film
made no direct allusions to genitals or concessions to their involvement in this heady brew, yet I had never felt so aroused or
so alive.

There came a point in the film when the type of woman, the
type of throat, that the filmmaker seemed to prefer above all
others, became focused in a single actress—a young, sullen brunette with delicate, almost plain, Renaissance features, she had a
strange aura that I believed I could actually see. Once she appeared, the film's splices stopped. When she finally spoke, reading
from a large, hardback tome, I recognized the dry, reedy voice
that had been a constant of the film's narration since its beginning:

'Tis now the very witching time of night,
When churchyards yawn and hell itself breathes out
Contagion to this world. . . .

As she read from *The Complete Works of William Shakespeare*, the low-
angled camera zoomed into a study—no, an unabashed revel!—of
her throat, celebrating its most apparent and most minute details.
I adored its swanlike simplicity, its mechanical complexity, its
damnable conundrum. Hers was the type of throat, with its skin
subtly creased across the voice box, that I claimed as my favorite.
I instantly loved the tiny, tawny birth-blotch covering the left
wing of her thyroid. My confusion intensified impossibly as I felt
myself painted into the film's most erotic corner. . . . And then
something happened to knock down the walls conjoined behind
me.

The camera was intent upon the visibly accelerating pulse in the woman's throat as the soundtrack swelled with a melancholy, instrumental jazz rendering of "I Loves You, Porgy." I suddenly understood, as the Glover's shadow darkened her shoulder, that the point of all the preceding footage—the *stare*, if you will, of all that had come before—had been to illustrate the Glover's slow, gradual *summoning of courage*. Without further deliberation dare was taken, taboo broken. The Glover lowered his mouth to the pale hollow of her shoulder and, seizing a pinch of skin between his eyeteeth . . . !

I was bowled over by how the film communicated, in that single moment, the courage it takes (a detail glossed over by every vampire film I've ever seen) to *actually sink one's teeth into the throat of another person*, especially the throat of a loved one, to set their life's blood flowing—and I was stricken by the selfless yet gratifying surprise felt by the young woman, receiving yet giving, so vividly conveyed that I felt her participation too. It was perfect, mutual sex; a stunning reenactment of nothing less than the first bite of apple in Eden's gone garden. The marks left on her tender flesh were not indentations, but rather an impression like a tiny necklace draped between her neck and shoulder; a rosary without a crucifix; each red bead in the chain forged from something more determined, more fervent, than repentance: the desire for oblivion.

This climactic scene resolved in the film's most famous image: a zoom shot onto the volume of Shakespeare's *Complete Works* left open on her lap, as the page on which the following words were printed absorbed a small splash of scarlet:

> If thou and Nature can so gently part,
> The stroke of death is as a lover's pinch,
> Which hurts, and is desir'd.

I remembered enough about Shakespeare from college to notice that, almost as a parody of the earlier splices that had prodded the action along from one point to the next, the text had jumped inexplicably from *Hamlet* to *Antony and Cleopatra*. With this puzzle left to perplex only a select few of its admirers, *Throat Sprockets* ended, the unattended flapping of the pickup reel in the projection booth sounding like a bat loose in the balcony. The houselights came on.

I was unable at first to budge from my seat, as if gorgonized by the experience into another stone cherub for the baroque recesses of the Eros's ceiling. Questions assailed me. How could anyone drink another person's blood as the culmination of an erotic and emotionally charged act, when movies since the turn of the century had devalued the potency of such a procedure into an unreal, juvenile cliché? Had the secret intention of horror films always been to keep the public in line by making this apparently transcendent act seem melodramatic and therefore inaccessible, unthinkable? Was Dracula no more than a propaganda messenger sent forth by a repressive society or government to keep the sexual imagination of the common man bridled, to keep his deepest reservoirs of fulfillment untapped?

"No more shows tonight, buddy," said a familiar voice, prodding me back into consciousness. The usher was pushing an ineffectual sweeper up and down the aisle nearest my seat, his clip-on bow tie held on at that late hour by a single clamp. "What do you want for six bucks, your bed turned down and room service?"

• • •

I decided to take a long drive. I couldn't go straight home, not the way I was feeling. I put the top down and drove out to a long, winding, little-used road where the dark was absolute at that hour, where the long-dead branches of parallel trees interlaced above the serpentine road, enclosing its motorized nomads in a vein of naked wilderness. Widow's Peak had been a personal touchstone of mine since my teen years. It is the talisman of people who don't move away to revisit their old haunts at will, places where important things have or should have happened, and Widow's Peak was mine.

Turning onto its summit and pausing beside the diamond-shaped STEEP HILL sign, I punched a Beach Boys song into the tape deck, one that I was fond of playing on this particular stretch of road. Existential questions sobbed from my speakers at top volume, asking how deep was the ocean, how deep was the valley, and how long would the wind blow; I began my descent. My next several minutes were spent speeding under a groined pavilion of naked, fretful branches, along every wooded turn of that complication of nature, cowing and astonishing its feral inhabitants—impassive owls, marauding raccoons—anything unlucky enough to challenge my headlights on frozen feet. Several steep climbs and drops beyond, the overhead lattice of branches disentangled as if their dark political deal had been struck, clearing for the most recent survivor of Widow's Peak a view of the city's skyline. Friendship filled the horizon like a dated postcard poised behind a single swaying traffic light, CAUTION its yellow advice.

I followed the signs back to the interstate, song segueing into song, the flashing sirens of each passing ambulance and police vehicle awakening in me the remembered color of the blood shed at the close of *Throat Sprockets*. It had not, I considered, been inordinately—*attractively*—red. The "sprockets" on the woman's throat had not been ostentatious, not the kind of garish latex appliance commonly used in horror films. Similarly, the Glover had worn no fangs to satisfy the conventions of that genre. But the fact to which I kept returning, perhaps because its implications were the most compelling and unsettling of all, was the drinking of the blood and how the film's various brunettes—they were all brunettes—had become more and more youthful, until they reached their ultimate convergence in the youngest of them all: the dark young lady sacrificed to the hands and mouth of the Glover.

And then, at once, I understood: No one, nowadays, would dare come into contact with anything but *virgin* blood.

This revelation fueled to brimming some inescapable questions: Between consenting adults (if indeed that woman had been of legal age), was the horror I had witnessed in *Throat Sprockets* necessarily a bad thing? Wasn't it said that any mutual act—that is, not forced by one person upon another—must be, by definition, an expression of love and therefore *moral*?

I pulled over to contemplate these matters and stood on weak legs by the side of the road. Friendship was still vivid in the distance, the few bright windows of its high-rise apartments at that hour suggesting neither harmoniousness nor shelter against the coming night, but reminding me of the collusion I had sensed in the trees interlacing above Widow's Peak, as if the same spirits that had enjoined those branches to lend danger to a road had moved downtown to draft a darker, more Draconian contract.

The young woman had not died from the encounter, I reasoned, nor had she been forced into its commission. On the contrary, she had *come*, she had undeniably come; I saw her mouth part into a tumbledown smile as her faceless paramour bussed her with his stained and busy little kisses, drying on her neck and cheeks in russet blossoms. I saw her deep, communicable sadness lift for a moment as she first set eyes on her valedictory gift, a choker suspended between the Glover's hands like a belt of indigo, which he fastened about her throat as both bandage and tribute. Its anterior surface was beaded like an Indian trinket, like Paige's own gooseflesh, the flesh-colored beads spelling no one's name, nothing to pin a dream on, only a terse dismissal: THE END.

It was *hard core*, all right.

In the meantime life pressed on . . . without convenient labels.

THE CABINET OF DR. ALIGHIERI

IN MY COLLEGE DAYS I WOULD HAVE RECOGNIZED THE NEED TO PURGE myself of dark thoughts and visited a friend for a late, unscheduled binge of squalid confessions—but all my friends had gone, in separate directions, to some world party to which opportunity and circumstance had not invited me. Some people are branded by their childhoods; all the scars I carried I had borne since adolescence, a period of life that I had denied myself in my eagerness for adulthood. Similarly, just as some people have fathers, mothers, brothers, or teachers who overshadow their lives —I had friends, the friends I'd had since adolescence, and they were particularly prominent in their absence. They were all a few years older than me, intellectual and artistic, and my admittance to their circle had consecrated in me an early desire to approach my life as an adventure in art; their departures, however, slowly enmired me in the necessity of passing the time in other ways, of making a living, feeling all the while like I was holding invisible tickets for detained trains at Friendship Station.

"But what about your wife?" a conscientious voice would sometimes reproach me from within. "Hasn't *she* affected your life?" Unfortunately, in those days, it was my curse to stand outside myself in relation to her as well; I was incapable of enjoying the things we did together while they were happening, of appreciating anything, really, until it was gone.

Paige, too, had an intellectual background but, unlike my male friends, she had been reared on different artists and authors and regarded my influences with wry suspicion. Music was our common ground, a force of art that unifies souls, but also a jealous communicator that prevents other voices from communicating at the same time. Though we never deliberately concealed our feelings from one another, everyone harbors a thimble-weight of truth from which we feel our loved ones must be protected, hideous snakes of thought that can be wrestled only in the presence of strangers with whom love is not an issue. The unattached may not realize that openness, in long-term relationships like Paige's and mine, often leads to *assumptions* of openness; the small anxieties of inner life can go undisclosed, remain withheld, become monstrous and deranged in the momentum of the status quo. Paige meant the world to me, which made the void I felt at the center of myself in the wake of *Throat Sprockets* all the more traumatic.

In the weeks and months that followed my first encounter with *Throat Sprockets*, summer phasing once again into autumn, I noticed some significant changes creeping into our nightly rituals. It had been our habit, for as long as I could remember, to read in bed together for an hour before going to sleep—me with my biographies, Paige with something more imaginary—breaking the silence between chapters with comments, gratuitous hellos, or sweet nothings, anything to crack the quietude of introspection. But after *Throat Sprockets* I suddenly became passionately interested in adding new chapters to my real life, the adventure at whose center Fate had specifically placed me. My memory of the film had assumed the talismanic power of a lover's photograph; it was something to be hidden in a rear drawer of my heart, to be taken out and studied, regularly and in privacy, something to jog powerful memories, to jog my heart, to remind me that I was still alive. And so I found myself adopting new habits, simply to break my former mold. I put down the lives of other men and began, in that hour before bedtime, to scan the dial of my stereo tuner, listening for voices and sounds that suggested a kind of sound-track for the potent images I wished to recall. Jazz was especially gratifying, as I could divine in the rumble and elegant persuasion of a four-piece combo the vague dimensions of a svelte and sym-pathetic companion, someone who could understand the strange grief I felt compelled to celebrate at the end of each day, each day being another brick in the wall separating me from the last time I had seen *Throat Sprockets*.

I was particularly fond of ballads, which were generally sung by women with loss in their voices and revolved around pleas for return, love tinged with remorse, and the inability to forget, the hard, hard *can't* of forgetting. But why, I often wondered, did I find lyrics about adultery so pertinent and affecting? I'd had sev-eral opportunities, even in my sheltered life, for affairs, and though I was prone to lose faith daily in all kinds of ways, I had steered sedulously clear of every occasion to be unfaithful. My devotion to Paige was boundless; my imagination, on the other hand, was a perennial rogue, never so much as betrothed. But now something had managed to collar my imagination. *That* was the source of my adultery.

Men cry, but we tend to be moved to tears quietly, as quietly as we masturbate. Men are raised to purge themselves in strictest secrecy, and I'm sure that Paige had no idea that I cried myself to sleep beside her almost every night of those months into autumn. My sleep, obtained only after draining away a heavy insulation of tears, was extremely troubled throughout this period, and I re-member waking from instantly forgotten dreams with a cotton mouth. I would climb out of bed around three in the morning, bend over the bathroom sink, and gulp water straight from the faucet, but no matter how much I drank, the water was never quenching. My insistent thirst subsided only when another inexplicable habit happened along to displace it.

I discovered, one night, that I slept much more peaceably while holding—no, *embracing*—my pillow. It was a habit that felt unseemly to me, especially with a wife beside me in bed, but when I dropped it to the floor and embraced Paige instead, feeling her warmth radiate from that deep place of sleep, my arms began to yearn for the passive coolness of my pillow, the satin-cased waistline and feather-filled hips formed by my embrace. I held out against the urge each night as long as I could.

During this period I continued to pay my visits to Widow's Peak, which I also used as a means of revisiting, *re-creating*, my wild emotions of the night I first saw *Throat Sprockets*. I was sometimes in a gambling mood and preceded my drives with a visit to the Eros, spending as much time as I could bear under the towering images of yet another skin flick that wasn't *Throat Sprockets*, that wasn't even close. Afterward Widow's Peak was always waiting for me; I tore down its sloping road, thinking reproachfully of my departed friends, and, after emerging from below its overhead tangling of branches, drove past all of our old haunts. My thirst returning, I usually stopped at Jesse's Diner, where the coffee was palatable, and drank a cup or two in the company of phantoms akin to myself, people eluding adventures of their own, or out at night in the hope of intercepting one.

There was a scene from *Throat Sprockets* that often came to mind as I sat in my booth, the one in which the Glover (the film's POV character) is acutely—even painfully—distracted in a sidewalk bistro by a brunette seated at an adjacent table, her throat framed like a tender target between the hard borders of her chin, her necklace, and two pendulous earrings. After a sudden SPLICE he observes the fanciful coruscations of light spangling the side of her neck, as it passes through the gems suspended from the ear on that side, and compares this to the rubescent light at play on his own tablecloth, refracted through the patterned crystal of his brimming wineglass. As if to discipline the temptation he feels, he rolls the stem of the glass between his fingers, applying more and more pressure until it snaps; the wine overturns, penetrating the linen tablecloth with a slow-motion torrent of port. Over the spill her deep purple eyes connect with his. The next scene is the first in which the Dark Lady appears.

Obviously Jesse's Diner wasn't a classy bistro where I was likely to meet such a beckoning creature, no matter what I might spill, but it had its good points. The acoustics allowed me to eavesdrop on the clandestine chatter of two fellow wanderers, talking through chews of coffee-soaked doughnuts, counting and re-counting the inadequate number of coins they had between them. I listened to their drama and watched the turning blades of a ceiling fan, mirrored in my coffee, going SPLICE SPLICE SPLICE. At the bottom of my cup there was always another ciga-rette to smoke, but after the length of that nicotine postponement there was never anything left to do but drive, drive on through the darkness that separated me from my wife and home.

• • •

All of the lights were out by the time I got back, and stepping into our five-room apartment was confusing at first, rather like trying to find a seat while a dark scene was being projected in the Eros. The light switch beside the door didn't work when I toggled it. On second thought I felt rather grateful that the lights were out and that Paige was asleep; my Adam's apple felt tight and constricted, and she would certainly have questioned me, would certainly have noticed the emotion in my voice and perhaps eval-uated that emotion as romantic distress. Even if she believed that she had no flesh-and-blood rival, *imagined* romantic distress—the kind that causes some of us to drive for long hours with only our own company to sustain the sweetness of melancholy—was in itself cause for concern. I thought I might sit and drink for a while in some dark corner of the living room and look a bit deeper inside myself, now that the responsibility of driving safely home was behind me, but I stumbled over something en route to the liquor cabinet and woke Paige. A click from the bedroom sent an angle of light into the area where I stood.

"Careful, lover," she called sleepily. "Don't break your neck."

I followed the light around a couple of painted corners and found her in bed, her nap-rumpled face trying its best to appear chipper.

"It's not my *neck* I'm worried about," I said. "Didn't we used to have something out there called a living-room light?"

"The bulb"—she yawned—"burned out, and since you never picked up any new ones like I asked you to do at least twice, I decided to hell with it, hit the hay."

I stood at the foot of the bed, rubbing a barked shin. I remember thinking that the ouch in my shin might explain the hurt in my voice.

"Besides, don't you know the layout of this place by now?" she continued. "I mean, we've been here three years—that's almost a year to get the hang of each room."

"Why, you calculating . . . !" I flung myself onto our bed and started tickling her. She was still groggy, and I took shameless advantage, but I stopped once her laughter edged into discomfort. She gave me a minty, sleep-soured, toothpaste kiss and we nestled in each other's arms, as I gazed passively at the calming of a pounding cord in her neck. Here was a person whom I loved without reservation; her ash-blond hair and its herbal-shampoo fragrance, her blue-green eyes and their astigmatism, the pigment dots that had surfaced on her body since we were newly wed, even the old Top Forty songs she sang to herself while stocking the dishwasher or reading submissions addressed to her attention. As much as I loved her, she had absolutely nothing to do with the fantasy creatures I had always claimed as my "type"—but Paige occupied my heart, not my head, and she seemed so blissfully unaware of the erotic ether shapes in my psyche that I relied on her to make me less aware of them too. There she was in my arms, trusting and available, but we both knew that it wasn't going to happen. A shadow I had brought with me into the room didn't lend itself to anything happening.

She asked if I'd eaten anything.

"Absolutely," I said. "Sno-Caps and jujubes."

She touched my stomach. "You're losing so much weight lately. You worry me."

I instinctively withdrew from the interrogative direction she was taking, and rolled off the bed.

"So how was the movie?" she asked.

I made something up, then turned the tables on her. "How was *your* evening? What did *you* do? What did *you* eat?"

"Oh, just another one of those fine Stouffer's products, and—oh, yes, you'll be very proud of me—I managed to work my way through that stack of stories you've been after me to clear off the TV."

"So that's why I didn't hear anything drop when I banged into it out there! How are the future men and women of American letters faring these days?"

"Let's just say I was reminded why they call them 'submissions.'"

"Oh?"

"Genuflections to the cold headstones of everything that's come before, every one of them."

"I'm sorry to hear it."

"There's nothing to be sorry about. As long as *The Goblin* can't afford to pay contributors, I'll have to read work by writers who find that arrangement acceptable. That's all there is to it."

"It's just that it pains me to see you spending your evenings reading the stale meditations of fresh kids, when you should be—you know—pursuing some meditations or genuflections of your own. You're only working at the university because I haven't been . . . well, moving ahead like I should be."

"What?" She sat up in bed. "Lover, you know that's not true!

That movie you saw tonight—it was *subtitled*, wasn't it? They always depress you."

"It was dubbed."

"Well, let *me* put some words into *your* mouth, because you don't know what the hell you're talking about. You're working for one of the oldest and most respected advertising agencies in the Midwest, which is exactly what we've been working all these years to achieve. Mr. Ingersoll wouldn't have hired you if he hadn't seen some talent reflected in your work, am I right?"

"The work I've done *reflects* talent," I admitted. "But it isn't talented work. There's a difference." I undid the knot of the tie I had worn since that morning.

"Hold it, I know what this is," she said. "This is thirty, isn't it? This is thirty. God, is this what I've got to look forward to? 'Midway through life's journey, I strayed from the straight path and woke alone in the midst of a dark wood'?"

"Thank you very much, Beatrice," I said sarcastically. "I'm not feeling sorry for myself. Just realistic."

"No, you're not. You're feeling . . . inhibited. But look on the bright side. You wouldn't be feeling inhibited unless you were somehow aware of the distance between where you are and where you want to be."

"Ought to be."

"Or ought to be. Right? Well, that's good, isn't it? And there's room for advancement at the agency. Mr. Ingersoll told you so at the company retreat."

"Yeah." I took off my shoes and sat akimbo on the involuted Indian carpet at the foot of the bed. Paige rolled onto her stomach and repositioned her face close to mine. "But what good is that," I asked, "when my ambition—" She rushed to still my lips with soft fingers.

"You're still my beau. Ain'tcha?"

"I 'spose." It was our kiddie voices. We had been married long enough to remember them, to remember each other's.

"All right then. Besides, I *like* working." She rolled onto her back, stretching and flexing her legs in the air. "I like reading, too, unless it's . . ." And she told me some of the lowlights of her evening's reading.

"Any howlers?"

"Oh, lots—but one was so wonderful, I memorized it for you." She rolled onto her elbow, her expression changing in an instant from that of a bedside confidante to that of a professorial mask poised above a lectern. " '*The street was literally paved with people.*' "

It was well after one o'clock but, after all the stress I'd been through that night, I doubled over at once, hurting with laughter. It was such a relief to feel all of my mind's blood and mystery dispelled by the laxative of a single inanity, to feel some kind of lifeline restored to my grip, pulling me back home from the void of deep space. Every time my laughter died down, I looked up at Paige, who was laughing at my laughing, and she made a face like the poached-egg eyes of hundreds of mashy, green-faced Gahan Wilson caricatures, staring up the trouser legs of oblivious passersby through miles and miles of clear acrylic boulevard—and I'd start laughing, helplessly, all over again.

"Well," Paige sighed when we finally calmed down, "that was *quite* a performance!" She wiped her eyes and crawled onto the floor beside me. She huddled close and looked at me for several long seconds with an expression that hovered somewhere between love and wisdom; I yearned for one and dreaded the other, which she must have seen. She was wearing one of my old T-shirts as a nightshirt; it was too large for her, rendering her figure indefinite, but as she leaned to one side, the slope of her shoulder slipped free of the neck, a smooth and fragile sculpture, cool as chalk and, where she felt a chill, bumpy like the bubbles in pumice.

"You really needed that, didn't you?" she said, meaning the laughter. I stared down at our Indian rug, feeling too tired to lie and too weakened to confess, but she raised my chin from my collarbone, commanding my moist and reticent eyes.

"It was—a sad movie," I lied.

"That movie must have ended hours ago. What were you out doing all this time?" I looked back at the rug. "You don't taste like John Barleycorn."

"I don't taste like pussy either."

She grabbed my averted face in her hands and forced me to look directly at her. "Hey," she said sharply, "don't hide from me, Angel Face."

"I went for a drive."

She paused a moment before asking, "Widow's Peak?"

I asked how she knew. She didn't answer for several moments.

"That must have been *some* movie," she finally sighed, scrambling back into bed.

I was drawn deeper into myself by the natural silence of our bedchamber, and stared into the ornate patterns of our Indian rug until its woven abstractions opened onto a geometric realm where questions and insecurities were left in the dust of soaring speculation. There, all things seemed as clear as they could be, and I could understand—without the tedious bother of *groping* toward an understanding—that, all in all, whatever I was experiencing was nothing new. Even in my parents' day it was not the exception but the rule for people to venture first hellos, to form relationships and unions, to found families, in fact, on the basis of how much the boy or girl next door happened to resemble their favorite matinee idols, how much those strangers happened to satisfy the hungers projected from Hollywood soundstages into small-town souls. If the mate dealt them by chance was not a perfect replica, or became less than magical as time wore on, they philosophized to themselves over a can of beer or a sink of dishes that life wasn't so different from the movies, that wedding bells often marked the Happy Endings of most love stories, that films faded long before the glow they sold as a solvent for ordinary lives. Rock was not yet an alcoholic, Doris was not yet unfaithful, and who everyone was to everyone else behind the DO NOT DIS-TURB signs of honeymoon suites—when each of us opens to another's scrutiny the horrid suitcases packed for us by formative events in our pasts—no one under the sun was ever likely to admit.

I had learned a few basic life lessons from the movies in my thirty years. The first movie I ever saw was *Blue Hawaii,* and it had taught me that women such as the intensely blue-eyed Joan Blackman could be wooed with the songs of Elvis Presley (a man so charismatic, I had imagined, that the Jordanaires had left their own wives and children to lend their chummy vocal support to his more important romantic crusades). Long after the movie had ended, one scene lingered in my mind, the one in which Joan lost her bikini top to the pull of the ocean. The King graciously recouped her flowered bra, gallantly reconcealing the breasts which—in my young and undernourished imagination—woggled in the warm Hawaiian tides as forms distinctly smooth and nippleless. And now, I realized—at least a decade since the movies had proved to me that women's breasts were pleasantly otherwise —that, though my knowledge had advanced, my original notions of *how women were* had not. I wondered if I hadn't been so deeply affected by *Throat Sprockets* because it had given this unfinished something deep within me, after all these years, the teeth it needed to access a body-temperate flow of nourishment.

• • •

This perception somehow used my sleeping self as a bridge to reality. It slipped outside my head on a ragged snore to trip my bedside alarm, which I had to scramble off the floor and across the empty bed to silence. It was the hour when all the things that bloom best in moonlight flee back underground or undermind, hauling their unraveled lengths behind them. I had awakened on my stomach, on the Indian rug on the floor, with a blanket from the bed draped thoughtfully over me. I was used to waking to wafting breakfast smells and the gurgling sounds of our Mr. Coffee, or to the noise of the construction team ripping up the imperfect road at the end of our street—perhaps to pave it with people, I reflected smilingly—or to Paige's playful goading, which always culminated in one of two ways. On this particular morning, however, the tinny clatter of the alarm had given way to no secondary sounds whatsoever.

In no particular order my thoughts touched on the likely events of the morning I'd slept through: Paige had already left for work, having thoughtfully reset the alarm to give me enough time to dress, grab a bite to eat, and reach my own appointments. Whenever circumstances robbed us of a morning together (conflicting schedules, broken alarm, sleeping too peacefully to disturb), it was our habit to leave affectionate notes where they would surely be found (coffeemaker, makeup mirror, near the john). On that particular morning it was the absence of any note that helped me to remember that not one, but in fact *several* days and nights had passed. . . .

And as memory returned, I realized I was in ruins. In willful denial of the details of our last evening together, I had spent the last few nights sleeping in the same spot where I had unintentionally camped on our last night together, going so far as to drape my own shoulders in a blanket as she would have done, in the vain hope that I might somehow pretend my way back into the past, that I might wake to find equilibrium reinstated and my marriage restored . . . but my eyes always reopened on a world in which the most horrible betrayal had in fact taken place, where she had been too frightened of me to say anything and had responded to my stammered apologies by holding a kitchen knife between us in warning. . . .

I ventured into the outer rooms of our apartment to find every vanilla cushion returned to its rightful place, the overturned table upright again; the signs of violence on the patio had been made as perfect and orderly as only scenes bidden farewell can be. All of her clothes had been removed from our closet. The car that I had driven to Widow's Peak on so many occasions, the very way into myself, that, too, was gone.

I have never felt any sense of injustice or offense at Paige's leaving. How could I expect her to understand, much less consent to live with, what I have been unable to accept or put into words myself for so many years? And after how many viewings of *Throat Sprockets*? Has anyone but God Almighty counted those?

It was not in my cards to be able, like most separated men, to blame the ruin of my marriage on work, or the tempting adjunct of a third party, or on the ways happenstance has of tripping even those of us who move timidly through life, planting one foot solidly in front of the other. With Paige and me there was never any question of overtime dubiously accumulating on dance cards, either actual or figurative. There were no strange musks to disrupt our loving collisions, no rendings—argued or unspoken—for us to immediately wish into the Never where we two lovers were bound.

My fling was with a *movie*.

I was never less than completely faithful to Paige, and I remained so for some time after she left, because in a strange way my fidelity allowed me to continue holding her hand. I felt that her presence, imaginary or not, was crucial to the successful compassing of an otherwise uncharted and dangerous course.

Those were terrible days. There were specific moments—in the shower, in the car on the day the radio reported, *Over half of the films produced before 1950 no longer exist,* while lunching at the Eros in the vain hope that lightning would strike twice—when her distant voice seemed to break through, into my new reality. That voice was strangely comforting to hear, not that I was putting comforting words in her mouth . . . quite the opposite. Whatever she was doing in her own life, Paige must have also sensed that a significant part of her life was missing, a part that I wasn't quite letting go, and she began to speak through it, tauntingly, as a ventriloquist speaks through a dummy, to utter insults to an audience he wouldn't dare address as himself. There was no doubt that it was Paige's voice, but she wasn't speaking to me. She was speaking *about* me to some unspecified third party, perhaps a girl-friend or a psychiatrist. What was most painful about what she said were not her accusations, but the fact that her voice, which I loved so much and needed so desperately to hear, was lacking all of the things I've mentioned loving about her, the things that used to tickle me so. Perhaps the shock of my disclosure had destroyed that part of her; perhaps she had been right to fear me. Her heart was gone from those aural visitations, replaced by a conscientious tone that discussed me with patience, a precision of focus, and absolutely no sense of affection or longing . . . rather like the passages of dissociated narration in *Throat Sprockets*.

• • •

I called him "Angel Face." It was what my mother called my father, you can make of that what you will. We were together for a long time, longer than some so-called successful marriages, which I suppose just goes to show you: you're never really safe.

Do you know what he tried to do to me?

• • •

His metamorphosis extended to his tastes in music. I should have noticed from that alone that something was terribly, terribly wrong.

One Saturday afternoon he rounded up about fifty of his albums and took them to a used-record store, trading them in for things he pulled from the Female Vocalist racks. He took to listening at night to Anita Baker and Sade, then to Sarah Vaughan or Ella Fitzgerald, all the great Ladies of Song. Then he moved into opera—sopranos whose names I couldn't begin to tell you. And I thought to myself, listening to this stuff from our bedroom, "Opera? Why the sudden interest in opera?" Of course it finally dawned on me, after what he tried to do that night. . . .

It was all throat music. He couldn't have cared less about the content of the music; he was after the substance of it, the texture, the sex of it, the husky vibrato. He was burrowing, digging, chewing into sounds, completely uncon-

cerned with melody, ignoring everything but the simple conceit that these sounds coming in moans and coos and wanton wails and soaring arias were an erotic discharge pouring into his ears from women's throats. No wonder he never looked me in the eye when I asked him to!

I'll bet if he were to get his hands on a transcript of what I'm telling you now, he couldn't tell you after reading it what I had said. The fact that it was a document of sounds from the throat of a woman, it wouldn't even matter whose, capturing a fleeting moment when he was caught inside it like a lump . . . !

• • •

I went back to the apartment the next day to get some things. In the bedside bureau I found a notebook stashed in the back, behind where we used to keep our valuables. It contained a lot of crazy words in Latin. Scalenus anterior, sternohyoideus, trapezius. I sneaked it to work with me, and my friend Jane—her husband's an intern—she told me that these were all components of the throat. It didn't surprise me. What surprised me was that they weren't listed only once; he repeated them in irregular cycles, until they became a chant. I stood there and read a page or two aloud and a very definite rhythm emerged. It sounded—well, like he was using it to masturbate, why lie?

• • •

I heard or imagined Paige's voice saying all of these things, and worse things that were also true. Nevertheless, I urged this voice when it came: Say what you will, give me your worst, but please don't disappear. Don't cut me out of your life; don't splice me out of your movie. Don't bury me alive in this black cabinet. Don't abandon me in this dark wood.

THE DISASTER AREA

THE PSYCHIATRIST IS NEVER FULLY SHOWN; IT IS LEFT TO US TO ASSEMBLE our perception of her from the isolated details of her well-manicured hand, taking clinical notes on a yellow legal tablet, the occasional icy peer over the heavy Italian frames of her eyeglasses, and her crossed legs. Scratches are visible under her nylons, like veins beneath translucent skin.

Only slightly more is shown of her patient. The brunette, perhaps in her late twenties (it's an early scene), appears to be in a state of exhaustion. Her clothes are crumpled and discolored, as if she has slept in them, as if she has been walking in them not only for miles but through nights and days of harsh rain. Her hair is in disarray, as if she has toweled it dry, and unmelted fragments of ice can still be seen clinging in places to its dark strands. She sits on the edge of the professional chaise—visible beyond her auditor's knee—as if shattered by a brush with some gigantic, unknowable experience.

The setting is scarcely believable as a psychiatrist's office. An enormous Pop Art poster is tacked directly onto the wall behind the patient, and the room is carpeted with orange shag.

The medium-shot composition (i.e., leg/patient/wall) is broken by a mosaic close shot of the patient, lasting approximately three seconds: a deliciously intimate anterior view of the patient's throat, vulnerable between the twin black wings of her hair, as she gulps back a welling tide of emotion. The previous composition is resumed almost before the eye can register the cutaway.

"Thank you for seeing me," the patient says, after a lengthy silence. In stark contrast to her emotional state her dubbed voice sounds incongruously placid and measured, like the paging voice at airports. "I need to talk to someone. . . . I'm not particularly religious, you know. Despite this"—she grasps the large silver crucifix dangling from her throat. "A priest wouldn't do. But now that I'm here, I don't know where to begin."

The psychiatrist suggests that she begin by describing herself and her way of life.

"I work at the university," she announces, "for"—one of the film's countless, confounded splices occurs here, obscuring useful information—"and the other professors in the humanities department. Perhaps because of the specialized nature of our work the women in the office all share similar life-styles or, at least, have views that generate interesting conflicts. So some of us have cultivated after-hours friendships. They've heard it all, believe me. If they knew I was seeing you! I can just hear Jane and Sally saying, 'You've got us—what do you need a *shrink* for?' "

Something overcasts the confessor's amusement; there is another brief, almost intrusively close mosaic insert as she presses her hand censoriously to her mouth. Another mosaic: something tenses in the vicinity of the bonnet string muscle of her neck, then gradually relaxes. Another mosaic: she wipes away a fugitive tear before it can ruin her rouge.

"I hope you don't mind if I ramble a bit," the dubbed voice continues, "because, to tell you the truth, I haven't slept in the last twenty-four hours, and if I were to draw a straight line from where I am to where I've just been—well, I'd lose it. Do you mind —I mean, would you read something into it if I touched myself *here* while I talk? It would make it all so much easier. I've hardly taken my hands off of it since—Not that I'm what you would call religious, as I say. But then, who can say whether a crucifix truly represents goodness? If it was my decision, I probably wouldn't wear it—but it's not really my decision, is it? I mean, wearing it. It was *bequeathed* to me."

She laughs again, at some irony that only she can recognize, then begins to cough. "I thought I was coming down with something last week, and I didn't think I would make it into work last Friday, as a matter of fact. That's a good place to begin, I suppose."

The psychiatrist grips the fleshy nub of her pencil's eraser between her eyeteeth. As the camera zooms into her eye, she nods in the affirmative.

"Not making it into work wouldn't have been a catastrophe, it was a Friday, after all. But it's easier for me to fight a cold if I don't let it take charge of my life. So I got dressed and made it into work about an hour late."

At this point the scene in the psychiatrist's office cuts to a dramatization of the recent past. We see a medium shot of the patient, seated behind the wheel of a car, itself a prop positioned before a rear-screen projection of snowbanked highway. Almost everything about her face is concealed—with oversized sunglasses, a heavy high-collared coat, and racing gloves—with only the V of her bared throat truly available to the viewer.

"I thought it might help to do things a little differently on the ride to work, just to shake off the malaise I was feeling. So I took a different route, thinking I might be stimulated by a change of scenery. I was listening to the radio, and sometime during the ten o'clock news the new route took me between two large hills that interfered with my reception, which began phasing in and out so badly that I couldn't hear anything but static. I arrived at the university about ten-fifteen. I kicked the slush off my boots and pretended to be coming back from the watercooler, slipping behind my desk with a preoccupied, already-working look on my face. I tried to hold my expression until somebody noticed and came over to get up a little girl talk, but everybody was circling around an invisible piece that was missing from the office procedure. It wasn't me, or the fact that I was late, but something that involved some unspecified point in my immediate future that I had yet to catch up with. My first impulse was to turn around and ask Janey who died. And that's when I realized she wasn't there.

"I motioned to Maria, whose desk is adjacent to mine, and said: 'Late again, I see.' Jane was always coming in late, playing hooky, you know the type. It was only after I spoke that I read from Maria's expression that"—SPLICE (and now she's speaking with great excitement)—"radio had been full of it but, as I told you"—SPLICE (and now she's mumbling with infinite sadness)—"It's just as well, you know, that I didn't find out with the steering wheel in my hands. Funny, but when Maria finally told me what had happened, it was like the world had somehow caught up with the way I'd been feeling inside all morning. I was feeling like the sound of Jane's voice when it was helpless and sad, when she crammed her mouth full of food to smother what she was feeling —like that day she let it slip out during car pool that she was involved with a married man.

"Most of us in the office knew that Janey had been seeing this guy and that it had been going on for a while, but she only mentioned it that one time. Maybe she hadn't meant to say anything in the first place. Maybe she'd had a dream that was about sharing something with me, and she couldn't stop herself from doing it because she was just following her mood. But she never spoke to me again about her love life. Maybe this had something to do with me, the fact that she didn't know whether my husband and I had divorced because of another woman so, you know— play it safe. There had been a couple of times, I know, when some of the others—who had been with the office practically since the time they graduated, like Jane—when they felt they had to say something about it, because whatever was going on was starting to interfere with her work. It was obvious that her situation was approaching a point of crisis. Privately, each of us, in our own way, sensed that something was very wrong and that something bad was going to happen. A broken heart, perhaps . . . but not this. Never this."

The last few words are spoken from an intimate mosaic view of her mouth, obscured by the hand of the nail it is biting.

The psychiatrist's free hand offers a cigarette to the patient. She accepts it. She lights it in the same close-up mosaic shot from which she has spoken previously. As the patient resumes her monologue, the scenes again cut away—this time to a scene of silhouetted violence on a penthouse patio, followed by a montage of newspaper headlines and TV news reports.

"It must've been sometime late Thursday night that it happened, or early Friday," she continues, exhaling the smoke. "I'm sure you read about it. Janey died when things got out of hand during some kind of rough sex with this guy, who's now under arrest. The police were reluctant to release any details, afraid of copycat incidents. The county prosecutor is calling it a crime of passion; defense is claiming accidental death and consent, hoping for second-degree manslaughter. I read in the newspapers that her lov—her *murderer's* wife—is in a state of shock. She had no idea he was into"—SPLICE—"or whatever they call it. She's so shocked, she hasn't had time to register that there was somebody else involved, somebody with a name, who had a life and friends of her own, who lost everything."

There is a shot of the patient's wringing hands, from which the camera dollies into a medium shot of a distinguished-looking man addressing the men and women in her office.

"Later that morning"—SPLICE—"came out of his office and begged our attention. He announced that Jane's funeral was scheduled for Monday afternoon, and told us where. He offered a brief tribute to her memory, said what a cheerful and good worker she had been and that she would be greatly missed, not easily replaced. What he said was certainly appropriate, but it left me racking my brain for instances when I might have seen him so much as *talking* to Janey, or taking any kind of professional notice of her at all. She'd been there much longer than me, so there must have been at least a few such moments between them. I mean, there had been instances like that between *him and me*—I mean, I *call* him by his first name. Anyway, he gave us all permission to return to our homes and spend the day in comfort with our families and that, in consideration of the national holiday the following Tuesday, there would be no office hours until Wednesday. I turned to Maria for consolation, but she was already gone. I remember thinking, '*So much for the Three Musketeers.*' "

The psychiatrist notes that tomorrow is Wednesday.

The brunette nods, as if wanting to hurry along to a specific point in her story, still not reached, while she has the necessary courage. The flashback scenes continue to unfold.

"The funeral was held in"—SPLICE—"yesterday morning, and we all drove there in our separate cars. I had been to the funeral home once before, a little over a year ago, when we went to support Janey during her sister's funeral. Something kept flashing into my mind throughout the drive there, something I'd overheard that previous time, when two men in attendance—friends of the family, I suppose—marveled that it looked like little Janey lying in that coffin; that's how much she and her sister resembled one another. I suppose I felt it wasn't any of my business but, my God, Doctor, why didn't I jump like some kind of oracle between them and yell, 'God forbid'? I wondered all the way out to"—SPLICE—"whether my intervention at that moment might have deflected the hellbent of history and changed everything.

"Once I entered the funeral home, I was overcome by something. Maybe it was the concentrated sweetness of the memorial bouquets, or the sign in the foyer that bore her name in removable letters, chosen from an assortment large enough to spell the name of anyone alive, or perhaps it was the cold winter day outside and the thought that every bird, every car, everything that constituted the hard facts of that day, was only a fiction from Janey's current perspective. It was a day on earth that she hadn't seen."

"Perhaps it was a day she was in charge of imagining," the psychiatrist helpfully observes. When no notice is taken of this pretty supposition, she sours her expression and adds to the vague scratchings on her yellow tablet.

"Or perhaps it was the unforeseen sight of everyone, all the co-workers who had defined my particular universe since my divorce, all standing around in mourning dress. It was like seeing how they would have looked, how things would have been, if—"

"If *you* had been in Jane's place," the psychiatrist observes. There is a close shot of her eyes, behind her heavy eyewear, peering closer, deeper, colder. As the patient nods without words in medium shot, the camera performs a sudden, incomprehensible zoom over her shoulder into the psychedelic heart of the pop art poster on the wall, providing a clumsy cutaway to the next flash-back.

In the following scene the brunette enters the funeral home (which has the same orange shag carpeting as the psychiatrist's office) looking noticeably more distraught. She faces a group of individuals, women and men peripherally present in the earlier office scene. "The people from the office greeted me like a stranger. There was absolutely no communication between us, between any two of us. Even Maria stood there like a stranger. Janey's death was cataclysmic."

The camera spins from one stony face, to another, to another. . . . "I looked at each of them, each in a different way, but everybody was equally withdrawn from me. I figured, *They've seen her; that's what it is. I'll view the body, then I can join them in their feelings; I'll be one of them again.*"

After holding on the last face the camera turns in a manic

cartwheel, which comes to a standstill in a long shot of the patient preparing to view her friend's body. She moves hesitantly to the end of a small queue.

"So I stepped to the end of the line, watching the mourners ahead of me as they made their good-byes in a variety of ways. I watched, unable to see more than a pale profile in the casket, as separations were tendered with a touch, a pained smile, a contemplative look, and sometimes with the gesture of the cross. One of her relatives collapsed into someone's arms after regarding her. The smell of flowers intensified as I neared the coffin. When it was my turn, I swallowed against the lump that had been in my throat since Friday morning, hoping Jane would wave a wand somewhere and dissolve it, and I—looked down at her.

"The lump stayed; I dissolved.

"Something was wrong, very wrong. For some reason the mortician had not been able to"—SPLICE—"Jane's throat. Everyone who came to say good-bye to Janey took an indelible, horrible image away with them. Janey had been put to rest in a child's nightgown, something her mother had picked out, and her head had been positioned directly, lopsidedly, so *hideously* onto her shoulders! Her neck was—almost completely gone—! Why hadn't anyone warned me?"

The body in the casket is not directly shown, but portrayed entirely from the facial reactions of the brunette mourning her. The image of her horror spins out of control, shifting to a placid image of the brunette having a solitary smoke in the snow.

"The next thing I remember, Vivian—Jane's roommate—found me outside, smoking a cigarette on a bench near the parking lot. I must have made quite a scene. We didn't know each other very well, really. We had met on two or three other occasions, the last time was only a few months ago, at the office New Year's party. That night Jane drank *so much.* . . . I had never seen her like that. I was just finishing my cigarette when I heard Vivian's heels on the gravel and saw her coming into view, fishing a pack of cigarettes out of her purse. She joined me on the bench without saying a word, except to scoot over.

"We smoked in silence for a while, just sat there listening."

"Listening?" asks the psychiatrist.

"To the sounds of the day. The day didn't seem to miss her. Vivian asked if I'd ever spent much time there in"—SPLICE—"and I said no. Some more time passed and then she said, out of the blue, that she and Jane hadn't been getting along, not for quite a while, and that she wished they could've had a few more laughs before she . . . but maybe it was just as well. Maybe things would have only gotten worse.

"I asked what had been wrong between them, and she said between *them*, nothing. Something about Janey's love affair had changed her. She had been behaving like a complete stranger in her comings and goings those last few weeks. Then Vivian asked me how well I had known Jane. I said, I knew her mainly from nine to five. She laughed at that, saying, 'Ah, you mean eleven to five!' And I laughed, too, because, as I say, Jane was never to work on time, especially lately, and I said, 'See?—You knew her better than I did!' I said that to cheer her up but, instead, it only made me break down.

"Vivian put her arm around me, threw my cigarette away, and let me cry. All these rhetorical questions were whirling around in my head. What had happened to Jane? How had she let this happen? Why was this breakdown happening to me? Who was I to behave at her funeral with less moderation than people who had known her longer, to be more upset than members of her own family?

"Vivian broke the silence by saying she didn't know how I was ever going to make it through the memorial service, going at this rate. I said she had a point, and as I felt her arm lift, I pulled out my compact and tried to fix my face. She asked if I still lived in"—SPLICE—"and I said yes. She reminded me that"—SPLICE—"was more than an hour away, and declared that I was in no shape to be spending that much time behind the wheel. To make a long story short she told me that she was spending the night with Janey's mom, and offered me the use of her place. She handed me a door key and told me to leave it under the mat when I left. So that's what I did."

The psychiatrist—a paralyzed pen, a furrowed brow—is stumped. Feeling as intensely as she did about the death of her friend, how could she have gone for shelter to the very place where she had lived, the heart of her existence, the receptacle of her associations?

"First of all, I had never visited Jane and Vivian's place, so there was no reason for me to be particularly disturbed by it. Also, she hadn't died there, but in her boyfriend's pied-à-terre. Beyond that, there wasn't much time to decide. Within moments the parking lot was besieged with an outpouring of mourners, some of them angling their cars to join the bumper-chain procession to St. Michael's for the memorial service."

The scene cuts to a close-up of a Saab speedometer registering eighty miles per hour. The disconsolate patient is at the wheel.

"I tried listening to music in the car, but the stations I found sounded either too callous or too sentimental. The jazz station was phasing in and out, too far away, and the classical stations were broadcasting symphonies that provoked images of celestial turbulence. So I switched off the radio and listened instead to the sound of my tires on the road. They were worn, but they were still here. Still moving forward. Like me. I held that thought.

"Vivian's directions brought me to a pleasant little residential area in"—SPLICE—"outside for a while on its front stoop, still concentrating on the details of the day, as if it was somehow my responsibility to memorize everything for Jane, everything about her old street.

"Can I have another cigarette, please?"

The psychiatrist nods to the pack on the table beside her chair. The patient chain-lights a fresh cigarette from its predecessor, and after a deep draw it shows a considerable curl of ash. White smoke dances in the room's semidarkness, an encouragement to introspection.

"So you went inside," the psychiatrist prompts. Half statement, half question.

"Why did I feel like a *thief*, Doctor? For going inside? For not"— SPLICE (her distress much greater)—"For surviving?"

"Have some water."

"Thank you. Anyway, the numbered door of their apartment opened into a long, narrow foyer. Framed photographs on one wall ran parallel with hooks on the other, where some out-of-season coats were hung. One of them was Janey's green mackintosh, which I remembered from that time my car was in the shop, a rainy day last fall when she gave me a lift."

"What kind of car do you have?" asks the psychiatrist. "What color?"

"A red Saab," the brunette replies, the camera focused for the length of that reply on a reflexive gulp in her throat. "Anyway, that was the day we became friends. The hook beside her mack was vacant, but I hung my overcoat and black dress-coat a space or two apart.

"There was only a faint suggestion of light in the apartment, which I thought was filtering through some open windows inside, but the light disappeared entirely when I closed the door behind me. In the darkness my awareness increased of a fragrance lurking in the place, like scented talc. The light switch beside the door didn't work when I toggled it. I thought I had seen a refrigerator somewhere beyond the wall of hooks—so I felt along the walls in that direction until I found it. I opened its door, which gave the immediate area a small measure of light and, just as important, a reassuring hum. Without it the apartment was unpleasantly quiet.

"After that I could see well enough to locate a corner lamp in the living room, which shed light on a small cabinet that contained the stereo. I tuned the radio to an unintrusive station, then doubled back to the kitchen to close the refrigerator. In the shadows behind its door I saw Jane standing—hovering?—in the corner. It was a bit like seeing a mouse; I got the hell out and left the fridge open. Janey was in the living room too—it sounds funny, doesn't it, the *living* room!—looking at herself in a full-length mirror. Her head was on lopsided, and she looked down the length of the childish nightgown she had worn to her grave, as if it were the long, tragic history of a country. . . .

"I can't explain why instinct drove me deeper into the apartment, and not out the front door. I remember biting my fist to gag a scream, and falling against this little open cabinet where they kept their liquor, upsetting a few bottles, but I managed to grab them before they broke. While clutching those bottles by their necks, I decided to keep my back turned to Jane, but as soon as I made that determination, I felt the spidery chill of her dead stare inching up my back on its eyelashes. Feeling that was worse than seeing her. When I finally got up the nerve to turn around, I was alone again.

"I poured myself a drink—neat and not very neatly—but couldn't swallow it. Once the drink was in my mouth, I literally had to squeeze my tongue against my palate until the pressure forced it down my"—SPLICE—"playing a Muzak version of 'Candle in the Wind,' but as the song went on, I began to hear words filtering through the instrumentation. I could hardly believe my ears: I was hearing one of our old conversations. We were in her car—I think mine was in the shop with a dead transmission—and it was that moment in time when she first became genuinely curious about me, my divorce, and my problems—I could hear her curiosity in the lilt of her voice—and I heard myself responding to her queries with pleasure and relief as we established the framework of our relationship, when I cast Jane in concrete as my listener. Then the tuner glided of its own accord down the dial to a classical station; it was playing an aria from *Lakmé*, which I had introduced to Jane on another occasion, when Maria was with us, which she later told me had become her favorite piece of music. I pictured her behind the wheel of her convertible on a summer afternoon, accepting that melody and the wrong man into her heart, and refilled my glass and drank it empty.

"My eyes skipped nervously from object to object. I was always afraid that the next object my eyes lit upon would be her. My gaze flitted from the TV to the VCR, to the liquor cabinet, the bookshelves, the video collection (only one or two tapes), the green walls whose velvet finish suggested billiard tables . . . with a chill of Janey hovering outside the edge of everything. Then it occurred to me that her presence was most apparent when I was most attentive and least in motion, so I decided to get up and move around.

"I found Vivian's bedroom, which was a mess, though I couldn't say whether this was due to emotional distress, or a hurried preparation for the funeral. In the room across the hall I saw Jane floating a few inches below a corner of her bedroom's stucco ceiling, a broken throatless piñata with nothing but presentiments to spill. The corner she inhabited was above the room's only closet, and I interpreted from this that she was trying to deflect me, to keep me away from certain things, the possessions dispossessed by the fact of her death. The ribbon on her gown was the ribbon at murder scenes that warns, DO NOT CROSS. I didn't want to embarrass her, but I had to know. I had to understand.

"I managed to reach that closet by staring at my shoes and telling myself, over and over, that only one shadow was on the floor. In the closet on wooden hangers were the dresses I remembered seeing at the office, some reserved for special occasions in polythene shrouds, recreation wear, shoes on a tree, more books on a shelf. Three untitled spines indicated photo albums. They were cold to the touch. I looked inside only one of them, and came away from it feeling dazed and ill, vague about what I'd seen, positive only that it had been some kind of—*personal material.*"

The camera begins to zoom into one of the photographs. The almost subliminal detail of Jane's throat culminates in a shock cutaway to a close shot of the psychiatrist's mouth. "Can you describe what you saw?"

We see the photos. "One of them showed Janey lying on the bed, her head dangling over the edge, so that her throat was stretched taut. Other pictures showed various objects pointed at or intersecting with her throat—fur, fingernails. I can't say they were pornographic, but I felt as if I shouldn't be seeing them, that it wasn't right to look. I turned the page and found . . . there were *thermographs* of Jane's throat stained with . . . well, a *man* had been at them. Suddenly, I no longer felt offended by the pictures; I felt only an overpowering sense of propriety toward Janey's survivors. I was seized by an almost irresistible impulse to destroy the photo albums and, just as suddenly, I felt a painful afterburn spreading through my throat. Cheap vodka, I thought. I looked up. . . . Jane was no longer a gloating gas above me. My increasing awareness of pain in my throat, like a force of memory, told me that Jane had somehow positioned herself *inside* me; I was carrying a dead baby. She wanted to possess me long enough to destroy those photographs and, somehow, my realizing this was enough to evict her spirit. I dropped the picture albums to the floor and got out, Jane gliding behind me from room to room, and I turned up the volume of the radio, turned on the television full blast, filling the apartment with enough sounds to drown out her pursuant laments.

"I looked for something hard and incontestable to grab on to, something incapable of death, something to give me the strength to stare her down until I was safely out of the apartment. The first object that came to hand was an oversized hardbound copy of *The Complete Works of William Shakespeare* from one of the living room shelves; I hugged it to me. This, for some reason, brought a smile to her lips. Then I saw this"—the patient again proffers the cruci- fix—"lying on one of the tables. It prompted a less ironic expression. I took this as an indication and held the symbol between us like a chasm. 'Why have you come here?' I demanded.

"And Jane *did* answer, her throatless voice extending less than a whisper but nevertheless reverberating deep inside me.

" 'I came,' she explained, 'because I *must*. Why do you ask?'

"And I said, 'I *must* ask!'

"And she told me, 'There is no answer.'

"We stood there, face-to-face, as different to one another as life is to death, until an alarming physical sensation reminded me that I was the only one with anything to lose. That's when I fled the apartment. I left every light on, the radio and the television blasting, the door wide open, and Vivian's key on the floor in plain sight.

"I didn't notice until the snow started falling that I was almost two miles away, that the book and this crucifix were still in my hands, and that I had left behind my black dress coat and my car.

"I hailed a taxi. Its warmth felt good. I blessed every block as it fell behind us, distancing me from that awful place. After a while, when the driver turned around and said 'We're here,' I realized that we were idling outside my *ex-husband's* apartment. Had I actually given my old address? Or was this another of Jane's manipulations? Had she appeared to forewarn me of something imminent? Was bringing me here her way of steering me from an alternate path? Whatever the reason I felt strangely comfortable with it. I could think of no one to help me through this but my husband. I needed him to help make sense of what had happened to me."

"And did he?" the psychiatrist asks.

We see the patient banging, banging, on the door in the gathering snow, until it opens on an absolutely empty, darkened apartment. She stands at the threshold, silhouetted. "He didn't live there anymore, he didn't live there anymore. . . . Unless someone he knows dies, Doctor, who will tell *him?*"

At this point her confessor pauses with a strained inability to answer. She sighs, looks inside herself, draws a blank. Then she asks the patient what, if anything, this strange episode has meant to her.

Once the patient resumes control of her emotions, she clears her throat—SPLICE—and fixes her auditor with sober and sensible eyes. The shot is peculiarly complementary to the earlier shots of the psychiatrist's tensely interpretive eyes.

"You've read Plato, haven't you, Doctor?"

"Plato?"

"I'm reminded of a passage in one of his final Dialogues, the one called *Timaeus.*"

"I'm afraid I don't know it," the psychiatrist admits, tilting her head to one side. (She is viewed from behind.) "Go on."

At this invitation the patient begins her solemn explanation, the camera dissolving from her speaking mouth to prowl through the highly magnified, convoluted details of the pop art poster.

"I don't, either, really," she says. "Janey was the philosophy major. But I seem to remember that, in this Dialogue, Plato said that the Demiurge provided us with a neck to serve as a sort of biological isthmus; that the throat exists to put distance between the head—the house of our higher soul, of our spiritual nature— and the body of our animal passions and appetites.

"What all this has helped me to realize is that there must exist certain stimuli—glances, encounters, passions that aren't impossible even for the most circumspect of us—which cause the signals of Mind and Body to cross. The neck makes it possible, you see. In the confusion wrought by certain stimuli the body may experience a form of arousal that seems to encompass the higher self, a lust so elevating that it feels like a form of enlightenment, redirecting the brain's former responsibilities to the unthinking, uncensored, primal regions of the gut. The concerns of mind and body were meant to remain mutually exclusive. But what if that mind is seized by the belief that the only love we've ever known must be sacrificed in the name of these newly awakened feelings? What if this redirected stimulation rocks us to our core, causing all of our faith systems to collapse? Such a catastrophe obliterates all self-knowledge, Doctor, and ultimately reduces us to our opposing components—Mind and Body—a divided self whose single skin is sustained, from that moment on, in a state of being pulled violently in two."

At this a tear literally springs from the speaker's eye.

"But we never tear, Doctor! We're just stranded forever in this— place, this in-between hell, this disaster area. . . .

"In the drama of our minds and bodies, our throats—which share the tissues of both, and the torment of both—the *throat* is the Disaster Area."

2

In the path of sin, only the first step is difficult. Has it not been said that it is easier for a woman to have no lovers than to have only one?

André Gide
Journals

TRANSYLVANIA MON AMOUR

CONTRARY TO THE REPROACHFUL VOICE THAT NARRATED MY LIFE FOR months in the wake of her leaving, Paige comported herself throughout our divorce with such an admirable lack of vindictiveness that *irreconcilable differences* seemed a vaguely fraudulent phrase. It was as close as she wanted our family and friends to be to the truth.

Who can explain how or why these things happen, but just as our separation had taken its legal turn, the Old Man noticed what he described as "a new strain" becoming pronounced in my work, something he hadn't seen before, certainly not when he hired me. Whatever he detected in my work during that distressful period impressed him enough to test me on a handful of hardball accounts. Colleen Sangster began to flirt with me more strategically. I worked harder, was promoted to an executive position, and earned more money than I had ever handled in my life. I spoke to someone who spoke to someone who had Ms. Sangster moved to another department. I gained a certain degree of recognition, graduating from being a fluke to being hot. Austin Ingersoll, who had against all odds kept his agency nationally competitive from its Friendship homebase for thirty-odd years without relocating to a larger coastal metropolis, had a provincial distrust of committee thinking; if we were judged right for an account, we were expected to take complete charge—from concept to completion. So it was that I was sent on my first business trips for the agency—to Cleveland, Detroit, and Baltimore. In short, everything that Paige and I had worked so hard to achieve during our years together started to happen with almost supernatural ease as soon as we went our separate ways.

Personally, I was drowning; professionally, I began to levitate. Regardless of how high my star was ascending, Chicago had been almost too much to hope for. Maverick Motors, the client in question, was headed by Lee Torrence, one of the Old Man's oldest friends; without this personal connection Torrence would certainly have chosen a more monolithic agency in a far more intimidating town to introduce his revolutionary new car—the Necromancer—to North America. It was my suspicion, during the weeks of rumor preceding Torrence's signature on the contractual dotted line, that the campaign would go to Nate Wechsel. Nate was SPI's top gun, a cool-tempered and charismatic man in his late forties, well read, well traveled, and soft middled, and the fact that he was an ardent racing enthusiast would hardly be considered a handicap. The Old Man, however, had other ideas.

Maverick Motors was the first SPI client, at least during my years at the agency, to inspire tooth-and-nail competition between its executives. Austin disliked competition, which he considered counterproductive among members of the same team. It was therefore company policy to assign clients and campaigns, without question or publicity, to the man or woman he considered best attuned to that particular job. Maverick Motors had to be handled differently, and a meeting was called.

Nate bottomed into his assigned chair at the roundtable with a smug expression that signaled to some of us that he had already been granted the campaign, confidentially, in advance. He didn't even lift his eyes from his folded hands when the Old Man ar-

rived in his characteristic dark colors to launch the meeting. The
wind blowing in from Lake Michigan was already whipping
through Nate's thinning hair.

"Each of you, in your own way, has expressed his or her desire
to take the reins of this particular campaign," Austin Ingersoll
declared, commencing the meeting. All of us men in the room
instinctively turned toward Myla Monteith, the only female executive in attendance, as if the *her* of the opening statement had
somehow been more indicting than the *each* preceding *his*. Myla
inclined her head so as not to return anyone's glance, but attractively, something flexed under the lateral aspect of her chocolate
scalenus posterior; she knew that she was being scrutinized.

"Of course, there are arguments in almost everyone's favor," he
continued, and the *almost* buried in that sweeping declaration prepared me to be the first to be disappointed. Regardless of how
exceptional my work had become in recent months, I told myself,
my promotion had been sufficient reward for that; furthermore,
this was an automobile account, and I was known to take the
Metro to and from work. To drive the nail deeper I considered the
stigma of emotional fragility attached to the recently divorced
and, finally and most plainly, I felt that Maverick wouldn't be
entrusted to me for the simple reason that I had never before
drawn breath at such an altitude. "But, following a generally
sleepless night," he grumbled on, "I've decided to take a gamble
on . . ." and stunned everyone in attendance with my name,
which resounded like an object struck at preposterous distance by
an arrow of indefinite purpose. Something also struck Nate
Wechsel, who held his winces well and kept mum, perhaps so
that others in his corner could protest on his behalf.

Myla had never been one of Nate's big supporters, but she was
displeased—as politely so as she could be—to see such favor
bestowed below a certain station.

"Nate," Austin addressed him, directly and not unwarmly, "you
know your job very well and with that knowledge should come

an awareness of its limitations and of your own limitations." He broadened his focus to address the whole room. "Obviously, Nate was the first of you whom I gave serious consideration for this project. And out of that serious consideration an important truth revealed itself to me. When Nate sits down to a new campaign and turns his key in the ignition, so to speak, he knows exactly where he's going and how long it'll take him to arrive. But this is the Necromancer! This is a completely new thing on wheels! Lee Torrence expects us to present it to the world in the spirit of innovation, not as just another of this year's models.

"Now, *this young man*," he said in a different tone, nodding in my direction, "takes a different approach. I've been watching him very closely. I've also had long discussions with him after hours. I know he's going somewhere. I'll warrant he knows it, too, but neither of us knows for sure how long his creative voyage is going to be, or exactly where it's going to lead him. I certainly don't mean to intimidate him, singling him out this way in front of everyone, but anyone who saw the work he did in those Children of the Night PSAs knows that his talent—or, rather, the *peculiarity* of it—could take him right to the top."

"I'm with you, Austin," Myla interrupted. "I'd be the first to agree that those PSAs were top drawer, but when all is said and done, will Mr. Torrence view them with the same gravity as, say, the work that Nate did for Pacific Lotion?"

"Or Myla's Amber Bars campaign, for that matter," Nate smiled, scratching her back.

"That's exactly why I've begun testing him on product accounts," Austin explained. "Nathan, old fellow, remember those boards I showed you for the Pfister Brothers account? You yourself confided to me that it was one of the best campaigns you had seen produced here in years."

"I assumed that was . . ." Nathan began, fading out as his eyes locked with Myla's. I smiled to myself.

"I know," Austin continued, "you're asking yourselves, What if this whippersnapper steers us into disaster? Well, boys and girl, we've survived disasters. This is Ohio, people. Hell, it's *Friendship*, Ohio. We can screw up royal, and nobody's gonna ride us out of town on a rail. But that simply isn't going to happen. At this particular juncture in my life, and perhaps more importantly, at this particular point in the life of this *company*, I firmly believe that the only way disaster fits into this equation is if we refuse to open our hand and let the dice roll.

"Nate, you're the best we've got when it comes to projecting prosperity and self-assurance. But that's not the Necromancer, that's *Chrysler* or some other goddamn—" The Old Man began to laugh, a sound that helped to vent the room's competitive chill. "In other words"—he cackled—"when Lee Iacocca gives us a ring, he's all yours."

I didn't want to get pulled into opposition with Nate or Myla, so I turned devil's advocate. "Austin," I interjected, "I appreciate the vote of confidence, really, but you know, I haven't even *driven* a car since—"

"I'm well aware of the fact that you're taking the bus these days," he allowed. "I can accept that. See, what this campaign needs is the vision of someone who dreams or fantasizes or, maybe better yet, reminisces about driving. You know, the way driving *used* to be—which this car of tomorrow makes possible . . . but not do it all cornball. You see what I'm getting at?"

"Yes, sir, I do."

"Then I see no obstacle. Here, let's give the roundtable a little taste of what you might deliver. Tell me this: What kind of associations do cars hold for you?"

"Associations?" The whole conference room was watching me.

"Yes, what might those associations be?"

"Well—" I considered this. "Getting my license."

He smiled. "Coming of Age," he bellowed, translating my association to the room. "And?"

"Well, there was this time when I was a teenager and driving on this long, steep road out on the east side of town. I was on my third date with—well, her name's not important, really. The accident wasn't my fault, really, but we got out of it without so much as a bruise while the other guy, he—he was drunk and ran into us. He was dead by the time the cops got there. We were pretty shaken up. My girlfriend threw up. I thought she was the one, you know? Her family loved me, they loved me like a son. But, after that night, after throwing up in front of me, I don't know, she was so embarrassed that . . . Well, we never went out again."

"Won't Maverick Motors love *that* testimonial?" Myla sighed.

"Surface thinking, Monteith," Austin shot back. "What you've just heard described in this all-too-frequently frivolous room is nothing less than Death . . . and Eros."

Despite my gloomy sentiments Austin's interpretations set me aglow. I pressed on: "And, of course, when my wife and I split up, she took our car. I think of that too."

"Separation," Austin intoned, with poignant finality. "So what do you think, Nate?" he asked, turning to his oldest colleague. "Coming of age? Death and Eros? Separation? This should be *one hell* of an original car campaign!"

Nate had nothing to say.

Which was how I came to be strolling through piercing winter winds outside the storefronts along Michigan Avenue. Paige's reproving voice had all but disappeared from my senses in the intervening year, yet small and potent reminders of her were sometimes conveyed to me by tentative transparencies in sight or sound that eliminated all time and distance between us. In Chicago her messenger happened to be the Doors' song "Peace Frog/ Blue Sunday," which I heard while warming myself over a cup of coffee in The Theatrical Chef; the musical ambience of the place was courtesy of a local "progressive nostalgia" FM station, whose playlist was based on alternative (i.e., nonhit) tracks from classic albums. I had introduced Paige to the Doors' *Morrison Hotel* album early in our courtship, and this particular suite became our favorite accompaniment to make-out sessions in her campus efficiency apartment, the first song's skiffle beat ideal for frisky foreplay, dissolving into a glittering ballad whose effulgence was perfect for lovemaking. I once described the melody to her, in a moment of verbal bankruptcy, as sounding like love.

"*Drug-induced* love," she corrected me, slipping a joint out of her jeans.

After that afternoon I could never hear the delicate, lysergic instrumentation of "Blue Sunday" without hearing the distant echo of Paige's sexy correction, and vividly remembering the courage it had given me to slip my hand inside her cords—which for us, at that time, constituted a brazen steal from first base to home plate. That memory, combined with the coffee's recharging of my batteries and the novelty of bachelorhood in the big city, sent me out of the bar into the cold, clear night with my determination to find companionship nearly as pronounced as my instinct for survival.

On my side of Michigan Avenue were the bright windows of shops, some of them flickering out as their proprietors locked up for the evening. Across the street the frozen surface of Lake Michigan spanned out to the horizon, as far and high as the limits of one's own concepts of adventure. On nearly every parallel street I encountered old abandoned theaters, as omnipresent as the city's own indigent, their black marquees no longer carbonated with the ginger fizz stardust of the fifties, sixties, and seventies, their razored screens showing nothing twenty-four hours a day to capacity crowds of rats.

That morning Lee Torrence had recommended over his eggs Benedict that I drive his test model around town to get the feel of the Necromancer, maybe take it up Old Town way, where he predicted I might find something worthwhile to pass my time. I expected Torrence or, at the very least, a representative to accompany me—if only to insure the safety of his prototype—but he

understood my appreciation of the solitary night drive. The Necromancer and its keys were delivered to my Westin suite within a
few hours of the last meeting of our first day. The damned thing
was red and it attracted attention like the Batmobile. I drove it
around for a while, rustily and not very well, and then ditched it
in a darkened corner of a Lake Shore Drive parking garage. The
prototype set me apart, and I was desperate, as a new traveler, to
feel as one with Chicago, to merge with Chicago. I needed *intercourse.*

I made my way up to Old Town. Its quaint specialty stores and
imposing memorabilia shops were curious, their displays visible at
that hour only through protective screen-grated windows. A book
shop called Back Numbers displayed some old sunned issues of
Playboy in their darkened window, a totem post of solicitous eyes
and lips from decades past, ghosts of adolescent lust bagged and
tacked to corkboard columns. A place proclaiming BEST PIZZA IN
THE WORLD was being kept open by a man eating single slices,
whose coat looked too thin to face the weather rattling its windows. I followed the last few evident lights to whatever curiosity
shops might be open just around the corner.

On the other side of that whim, in a secluded, renovated alley
with brick pathways and inner-city tree stems, I found myself
outside a tiny shoe-box cinema, no ginger fizz bubbling around
its marquee but nevertheless open for business. An improbable
sight, it stood out in the biting winds like a mirage.

It called itself the House of Usherettes. It only took a peek
through the front door to sell me the ticket. One usherette was
on call to open the door; another waited with her hip roundly
jutted against a wood-grained container for torn tickets; another
leaned with large loping breasts over the candy counter at the
side of a fresh-brewed coffee concession; and yet another waited
with both fists wrapped around the silver shaft of a flashlight,
ready to escort the next patron into the dark depths of the auditorium beyond. Each was costumed in exquisite French lingerie, of

an exclusive color particularly suited to her personality, and wore a blue elastic collar embossed with the name of the sixties starlet she most closely resembled.

I stole inside the lobby as quickly as I could manage, not wishing to expose the barely clothed attendants unnecessarily to the cold air outside. The warmth inside was immediate and unreal.

"Good evening, sir," chirped "Pamela Franklin," her dark brown hair framing a natural, wholesome, English complexion. "Welcome to the House of Usherettes."

After tearing my pink ticket along its perforation "Yvonne Craig" returned my stub with her trademark pout and arched eyebrow, and the "Stella Stevens" at the snack bar followed me with soulful stares as I cut a path directly toward my choice of entrances, where "Barbara Steele" nervously stood guard, biting her lower lip. I asked to be seated in the smoking section. She looked at me dead in the eyes and said, as if I'd spoken in code:

"Oh—I get you."

Judging from its trim and economical interior the House of Usherettes seemed to be a 1970s screening room refurbished within the last few years with black, capaciously cushioned rocking seats. My escort directed me to a place near the halfway exit, pointing her flashlight beam to an aisle left of the screen, where almost no one else was seated. The smoking area was clean, each chair smartly equipped with a compact ashtray built into the back. I took a seat and searched my pockets for cigarettes.

My pack was empty.

The film had not yet begun, Paige's voice intruded, sarcastically reprising the narration from an appropriate scene from *Throat Sprockets*. *He considered going to the cigarette machine, but saw that the situation provided an opportunity to brush against others in the trenches.*

I noticed a woman seated alone, smoking, three rows ahead of me. From where I sat I could see that her hairstyle was short, displaying a slim patrician neck. Her mode of dress was businesslike and I thought she might be an out-of-towner, like myself, trying to put the evening out of its misery. I couldn't see her face, but it didn't matter what she looked like; what most excited me at that craven moment was the opportunity to play the lead role in a film I adored. I exchanged my seat for one directly behind hers, taking advantage of the patient silence in the auditorium before the film began to lean into her ear.

"Pardon me," I quoted, "but could you spare a cigarette for a dying man?"

Without a word, having barely turned in my direction, she unfastened her bag, found one, and fired it up for me.

She doesn't even smile. . . .

I thanked her—who can explain why men do these things for women?—with a courtly bow.

So he assumes she isn't interested. . . .

I settled back in my seat and drew the smoke into my lungs as the pleated curtains opened with a lazy, skirtlike swing.

But the tip of the cigarette she passes you in the dark is wet. . . .

I smiled, deeply gratified that the moment had remained consistent with the dialogue I remembered from the film, amazed to be swapping spit with a stranger in a Chicago theater. The film being shown was *Transylvania Mon Amour*—the title clumsily inserted on a shiny white card—but there was no doubt, after the first few seconds, that it was *Throat Sprockets*, playing in disguised rerelease. Under how many other titles had it existed? Under how many other titles had I missed it?

The unexpected pleasure of being reunited with *Throat Sprockets* was only intensified by the discovery that each of the splices I remembered from the ragged print that had played the Eros, two states away and four times as many months ago, was present in this second print as well. My pleasure was somewhat mitigated by the fact that the scene of the hotel tryst was missing—no doubt excised for some projectionist's private collection—but there was the added compensation of a scene that had not been included in the Eros print: the neck rub. I watched the film with a smile that openly acknowledged that anything was possible.

So he knows to wait.

Before the film had quite ended, I sneaked up the aisle and asked "Stella Stevens" for change for the cigarette machine. The woman in the trenches exited the House of Usherettes, walking straight into my hand, extended in the offering of a single cigarette. Her brand. Consolations.

"Dying?" she quoted.

"Dying," I replied, "for a cigarette."

She narrowed her green eyes at me, a gesture that was in her case closer to a laugh than a sneer.

• • •

While researching my PSAs for the American Cancer Society I had learned that nicotine is addictive because it acts as a barrier against stimulus; it allows the user to function in overstimulated environments and situations with calm and self-assurance. Nicotine withdrawal is like losing a protective skin over the nerves; it brings the smoker closer to emotions. Catch a movie producer on the phone and tell him his piece-of-shit sequel is a rip-off of your agency's award-winning commercial, and he'll ask you to hold on while he gets a cigarette. Hospitals can't deny cigarettes to their patients because they don't deny them to their doctors. Not only does nicotine soothe (and eventually cancer) the savage breast, but smoke creates a suave atmosphere in which one can function bravely, gracefully, falsely. It is one of the lies that bring us peace, lulling our trepidations about the possible consequences of animal heat.

True to my instincts this movie-going acquaintance was a fellow business traveler, someone who regarded Chicago less as a city than as a vast annex of O'Hare International Airport. I doubt that she truly believed this, because neither of us was being candid about our names or our opinions; everything we said about ourselves was deliberately explosive and outsized, mysterious and enterprising, correct only to the extent that it was self-specializing or illicitly tantalizing. She knew where to catch cabs at crazy hours; she knew of a safe recess along the lake where we could smoke and talk about destiny without being molested by passersby; she knew where we could get the best java in town and go straight from our booth to the registration desk of a respectable hotel without having to step back outside. It sounded like a nice evening, any of those evenings, but being young and impatient, we seized upon what was closest.

Under the harsh lighting of the Backstage Café I saw that my companion wasn't especially like Paige or my "type"; she was attractive, but there was something decidedly severe about her looks. Her dark auburn hair was styled into a vaguely punkish wedge with guillotine sideburns, she wore eye shadow the color of red cabbage, a color scheme perpetuated in her neckerchief. The corners of her purple mouth resolved in embittered curls. We ordered coffee. Coffee: it gives two mouths, up till now estranged, a common taste of earthy darkness. It encourages us, like cursing. It gives us a reason, besides the obvious—which we deny —for our giddy hearts to be racing.

She asked if I was married. I still hadn't removed my wedding band, so I gave the easiest explanation, that I was. It was a lie that she seemed to like.

"What's your name?" she asked me.

I thought quickly. "Wechsel, Nate Wechsel," I said.

"Mine's"—long pause—"Nancy Reagan." She grinned.

"Oh, no, it isn't."

"Believe it. I get this all the time, as you can imagine. Try and get taken seriously in the world of big business with a name like Nancy Reagan. You have to be ten times as aggressive just to fall behind."

"Then the same thing must be true for the other one too," I observed. Almost as soon as I'd said it, I saw that this lady was after a sympathetic hookup, not another laughing boy executive; I paused for the length of a sip of coffee. "Don't worry," I said, coming up for air, "I take you seriously."

"You take *the opportunity I represent* seriously," she clarified. "When precisely did I become an opportunity for you, anyway? During the movie? After? Or was it as early as the cigarette?"

"But the tip of the cigarette she passes you in the dark is wet," I quoted. "And what about you, Ms. Reagan? You're sitting here with me in this booth; what was it about *me* exactly that you responded to?"

She squinted at me, I suppose to sharpen her focus; when her nose wrinkled, I could see small viselike imprints on either side of the bridge of her nose. She wasn't wearing her glasses. "I dunno," she said, sizing me up. "There's something sweet about you. Like you can't stand your own company. Somehow, that's very agreeable to me. I can't stand my own company most of the time, but I could probably stand yours. I could sort of stand a change . . . if you know what I mean."

We left some money on the check and ran together into the night.

• • •

The LaRonde Hotel happened to be on Lumley Street, which inspired us to launch under moonlight into a perverted duet: "It's down at the end of *Lumley* Street . . ." Our cold breath commingled in the night air. The carpeting that poured along the hall to our room absorbed our footfalls complicitly, having witnessed enough misadventures amid the passing parade to anticipate and muffle the sounds of weak, backsliding flesh.

Inside the room we reclined together, facing one another from opposite ends of a king-sized bed. She had draped her blushy scarf over the bedside lamp, incarnadining our arena with an evocative roseate tint. She licked her lips and said, "Tell me what you like, Nathan."

I thought of the green-foiled mint resting, across town, on my hotel-room pillow; it was a green light to all this, a permission to drive through anything to reach it, just to get back there. I responded to the luxury of Nancy's question—which made me feel for a moment that anything in her particular candy store could be mine for the mere description—by saying, "I like coffee . . . good coffee. . . . I like to watch good coffee being poured . . . and I like women who taste like coffee . . . coffee or tomatoes . . . and smell like fresh bread . . . warm, yeasty, risen."

Nancy Reagan's eyes leered knowingly past mine as she rose from the mattress. She walked into the adjoining kitchenette, where I heard the room's percolator being readied for use. Then she disappeared into the bathroom. Our den of portent was soon filled with richest aromas of home, another transparency through which Paige was fleetingly visible. Nancy emerged from the bathroom naked, a long and thirsty hotel towel wrapped LaRonde and LaRonde her.

She found her way back to the kitchenette and soon after edged back into bed beside me, holding one cup of coffee prepared especially for me. Gratefully, I took a sip and placed the cup on the bedside table, as she resettled in front of me, tilting her head to one side to proffer her slender throat in its lateral aspect. *Reward me*, it seemed to say. The usual images—who doesn't have them?—flooded my mind. I lingered over her jugular notch and, hesitantly, kissed it. *Now that my balls have brought me this far*, I thought, *what is my mouth going to do with you?* I backed off, taking another sip of coffee.

She turned on me reproachfully. "Look," she spat, "suspense is for Hitchcock! We met at the same movie, right? So what the hell's stopping you? I know you *want* to." Again—this time more insistently—she inclined her neck to me, looking away like a child awaiting the prick of a hypodermic needle. "Do it!" she commanded.

I watched her hastening pulse and sought the right words to express the conflict I was feeling, dizzy before its abyss. "This is going to sound strange," I warned her, "but somehow, *not* doing it is the only thing that's keeping me alive."

"What?"

"If I were to do what you're expecting me to do, then every-thing—*every thing*—will change."

She turned on me with a vivid expression of invitational joy. "That's exactly why we *have* to," she explained. "Don't you fucking see that?"

She took my head in her hands and pointed my eyes toward her throat, saying, "Bump bump, bump bump," as she playfully flexed her sternocleidomastoideus, amplifying the natural rhythm of her pulse to allure me. Then she stood up and, letting her towel fall to the floor, began crawling toward me across the mattress.

"You know, José," she chuckled in a macabre singsong, "I've got an early day . . . so what do you say . . . we get the old ud-blay . . . outta the way? Okay? Bump bump? Bump bump?"

She modeled her throat for me, flexing her neck from its ante-rior to its lateral aspect. I couldn't help admiring the way it poured into her shoulders, its fine edging of down visible in the fevered lamplight. Her eyes opened next to mine, glimmering as mine feasted.

"My friends tell me I should go far. . . . An ambitious girl should have it in her repertoire." She traced her neck with a well-manicured nail, bearing only a teardrop of red polish. *A red sob,* I thought.

I presume that the look on my face was baleful; something she saw there sobered her.

"Hey, wait a minute—you're really scared, aren't you?" she real-ized. I said nothing. "But I can tell that you want to."

I admitted to thinking about it.

"There you go," she said, encouragingly. "Wouldn't you like to get those nasty thoughts out of your mind and into the real world? I know exactly what you're thinking of, lover. You're thinking of that scene in the movie. . . . You know the one I mean . . . that scene in the *hotel* . . . ?"

Her eyes blazed the color of greenfoil.

Inside the bedside table drawer—beside the courtesy condoms —was a sealed compact containing a small assortment of oral prophylactics. These were to be worn around the head like a bandanna, under the nose on the lower half of the face, and they came with a small pocket that fit comfortably inside the wearer's mouth, allowing the jaw to maintain complete freedom of move- ment, and its toughness was such that it was impossible to bite through. Also provided was a pair of gloves made of the same white rubbery material, a packet of antiseptic wipes, and, for the truly conservative participant, a foil packet of antibiotic dots the size of sugar pills. The manufacturer's name was Cross; their cor- porate logo, warding off the pollutions of a so-called "vampiric" life-style, did not look at all out of place beside the Gideon Bible. My partner insisted that she was perfectly safe, but stressed that these devices were intended for *mutual* protection and patiently described the procedures of "sprocketing" with such clinical preci- sion that it was hard to accept that this was to be her first time as well . . . but there was no faking unviolated skin.

The orientation process completed, she resettled into position as I wrapped the crackling, elasticated mask about my mouth. It was as tight as a second skin, and I was surprised to find that the prophylactic did not impede my powers of speech, but rather bestowed on my every word a peculiarly arousing, vibratorlike buzz. The woman felt the Glover's hand attentively trace the lines of her trapezius as it swung into her shoulder.

He spoke: *I once knew a certain woman—*

"Oh?"

—who had an extremely sensitive neck.

"Tsk-tsk."

It was long and fair skinned, blue and white like a robin's egg.

"Ah."

But her skin had certain—ticklish spots.

"Mm-hmm."

Such tender places—that not even her husband *was permitted to touch them.*

"Uh-oh . . ."

Those spots were so sensitive . . . so tender . . . so responsive . . . that to brush them . . . even accidentally . . . caused them to blush . . . like a robin's breast.

The green was goading. Before I understood what I was doing, I had seized a pinch of her skin with my eyeteeth. The only sound she made was a swift intake of air. The almost instantaneous welling of blood against my mask, darker hotter stickier than I had expected, startled me. Despite my measures of protection I couldn't quite bring myself to open my mouth at first and then, in my excitement at her volume, my tongue became tangled in the pocket inside my mouth and I couldn't swallow her—so I simply nuzzled her burbling warmth with closed lips. Even this contraceptive contact had an unexpected kick; my ears burned, my hearing thickened in a sudden swoon, and I felt a mysterious impression of current in my armpits. Somewhere far away I could hear her responding with chanted words, all over me, rising, all over me, in different tempers, then in different voices. Choirgasm!

I was slapped back to my senses.

"You asshole," she hissed, clamping the LaRonde bath sheet to her throat. "You got it all over me! Ohhhhh, shit! You wouldn't *swallow* me, you wouldn't fucking *swallow* me!?"

I tried to explain, but found it was impossible to speak with my tongue caught inside the pocket. I ripped the apparatus from my face, the snapping of its rubber splattering us both with the scarlet pittance it had absorbed.

Nancy scrambled to her feet with the extravagantly stained luxury hotel towel trailing from her like a banner of Mother Victory. "Listen, Thoughtful," she said, "yes, I've been around, around long enough to know that nobody—nobody—gets *anywhere* without taking some risks."

She stormed into the bathroom, ran the taps, and eventually reappeared, redressed. She took the neckerchief overhanging the lamp, transforming the ambience of the room with a quick tug from fervid red to pallid bled. With the scarf rearranged about her throat, and her glasses on, I realized that Nancy Reagan looked much like any one of a hundred women I'd seen in office buildings and hotels and airports since the agency had started sending me out on the road. Her bespectacled eyes were livid as she threw on her coat and lit a cigarette.

"Thanks for breaking me in, sport," she sneered. Halfway to the door she pivoted toward me. "You know, I plan to be one hell of a CEO someday and—oh, what do *you* care? You're probably already there, aren't you?" She flicked her cigarette at me and was gone.

I hugged a pillow until the sound of the slammed door stopped ringing in my ears.

Have you ever had the experience of remembering yourself, standing in a room you can no longer place, somewhere you couldn't find your way back to if you tried, revealing secrets about yourself to people you no longer know? It's the most frightening feeling in the world.

As dawn suffused the horizon with a natural roseate hue, I watched her leave by taxi from the window. I wondered where it would take her. I wonder where she is now. I wonder if she breathes there.

And then Yours Truly, globetrotting executive and carnal roughhouse epicure, padded across the piled carpet to the bathroom and slapped on the lights. In the full-length mirror I saw a naked surprise with numb, milky eyes and electrically missorted hair, blood all down my shallow chest like a clown's trick necktie. And, I swear to Christ, the bathroom I saw in that single glimpse looked perfectly white in contrast as I fell toward the toilet, but when my eyes rose brimming from the sin that came up, the walls around me seemed to absorb a venal darkness, besmattered with pernicious excrescences, atavistic graffiti and portent. I rinsed my face in a browned basin, noticing that the tiles around the shower no longer shone, but lay dull and dead under a skein of time and dust that was indistinguishable from human tissue.

And I thought to myself, *It is. . . . It's* better *with someone you love.*

• • •

Nancy Reagan had left it to me to settle the bill, and the clerk caught my attention by clearing his throat as I slipped my gold card from its wallet window. He mirrored himself to me by subtly indicating the edge of his mouth with a well-manicured pinky; I understood and, with a handkerchief, daubed an overlooked blood fleck from my frownline. The clerk accepted my card, and the twenty-dollar bill tucked discreetly beneath it with one smooth, accustomed movement. I thanked him, and he returned my carbons.

"LaRonde looks after its customers, sir."

I taxied back to the parking lot on Lake Shore Drive, where I found the Necromancer's security system shrieking. During my absence someone in gloves had siphoned enough fuel from its tank to give Lee Torrence, the next day, the convenient impression that I had driven all night long in his brainchild. I climbed into the cockpit and felt, like an emanation from the backseat, the past presence of a gloved intruder . . . the insertion of his si-phon . . . his anonymous lips fastened on the outer end of the hose . . .

As my key card opened the door of my room at the Westin, the angle of light from the corridor fell across the green-foiled mint on my pillow and it came to me.

I knew how to sell their bloody car.

• • •

My return to Friendship coincided with the weekend that, for lack of any greater compulsion, I used to sketch out my ideas for the Necromancer campaign. *Ideas* hardly seems the correct word; whatever they were, they seemed more an expression of my body than my mind, evolving from the unguided scribblings of my pencil into something that was so expressive, so resolute and self-contained, that it scarcely needed the mindful effort of a slogan to put its message across. Saturday and Sunday were swallowed up in a blur of mindless, intensive industry.

Monday rolled around before I knew it. The Old Man understood the creative process and was used to catching his employees in the act of daydreaming; it was acceptable behavior, an occupational hazard that he regarded in the spirit of a blessing. I was hunched over my boards and must have been staring into space for some time.

"Lost in thought?" he asked.

The Old Man repaid both honesty and bullshit in kind, so I admitted to being "just lost."

Austin didn't dwell on this. "You're entitled," he supposed. "So tell me, how was Chicago?"

Before I could answer, he slipped the boards from under my elbows, his wiry agility faster than any unfocused objections I might have had. He flipped through the four preliminary panels I had prepared and shot me a look of pleasured disbelief, which then exploded into a broad grin, an aurora of avuncular delight.

I can still see him lingering there, one of the richest men in the state, admiring my work with that ever-dilating expression of satisfaction he had, squeaking like a well-worn floor without having done any of the pacing. He held up the concluding image—the "resonance of the piece" as he liked to say—so that I could see it from across the room, actually making my own presentation to me.

"This is incredible," he beamed, calling me by name. "FIRST EPISODE . . . 'GO TO HELL'. . . . A LONELY ROAD . . . DRIVE A SPELL—NECROMANCER," he read in his best James Earl Jones baritone, allowing my tag line to resonate.

"That's . . . what the man . . . wrote," I stammered, deeply disturbed.

"I'll bring these right back; I want Nate to see them," he announced. "DRIVE A SPELL," he repeated, relishing the act of repeating it.

I had slaved over those boards head-over-heels, upside-down, ass-over-tea-kettle, and sunnyside up. Not once during my weekend binge did I recognize the subtle creasings and fissures of human skin in the sun-baked desert highway of my final panel, or notice in the flaming tire tracks of my zooming Necromancer the parallel patterns of bleeding film sprockets. The dangers present on either side of the road—the rattlesnakes and vultures, the cattle bones and what-have-you—those were my own clichés, but as the Old Man held up my boards to me in his proud paternal paws, I saw all too plainly that my campaign was little more than a *tracing* of the original poster design for *Throat Sprockets*.

MERCHANDISE

O ONE EVER SAW—AT LEAST NO ONE EVER ADMITTED TO SEEING—THE stark similarities between my Necromancer campaign and its unconscious antecedent. The Necromancer went on to become the phenomenon that it remains today, despite its perennial condemnations in *Car and Driver* as a gas guzzler. Against all expectations Austin traveled to New York City the following spring to accept a brace of Clio Awards for the print and television adaptations of my concept. Not long after that many of New York's top businesses followed Lee Torrence's lead by taking their advertising business to Ohio. When *Adweek* declared him "Advertising Man of the Year," the Old Man issued the following remark to his interviewer:

You folks in New York and Los Angeles, you are who you are. You live with yourselves every doggone day. We folks in Ohio only see you folks on television, so we have to *imagine* who you are. That's the nature of our relationship. Your cities may be the muscle and the nerve centers of our great country, but you need the *imagination* of this country to give you direction, to tell you what can be done with those hammers and those nails in your hands. The way things have been set up, up to now, has been wasteful. Why should Ohio, or Indiana, or Kansas for that matter, continue to relocate its most gifted sons and daughters *en masse* to these already overburdened nerve centers? It's less stressful and more expedient for all concerned if you major cities take a taste of humble pie and start looking for your answers where they've been contemplated all along. Don't go to the man who's so rattled that he jumps out of his skin when you tap him on the shoulder. Go to the man who sits on his front porch with his nose in a book and an eye on the horizon. So, to answer your question: No, I'm not in the least bit amazed by the recent success of Sutton Perry & Ingersoll, only by how long it took New York to discover that the telephone (which is only about a hundred years old) rings both ways."

I call him "The Old Man" out of affection and distance, but during this period Austin Ingersoll was only in his middle fifties, his Swedish fleece white since his middle thirties. Success was a quack of fate that goosed Austin out of his provincial complacency; to perceive one's enterprise for so long as fully grown and then to be catapulted beyond those accepted limitations at the close of life's Second Act had knocked him for a loop. His clothes changed from the dark-suited adornments of middle-aged conformity to a retro Carnaby Street assortment of purple shirts and white neckties, and the front-porch wisdom he adopted as his public image staged a quiet, benign takeover of the Austin Ingersoll we used to know. As for me, I was rewarded for my involvement in Necromancer and one or two other major accounts that followed with a significant raise in pay and a new office, complete with a panoramic window seat cushioned with black-grooved, burgundy corduroy.

Time passed, and the sonic boom of SPI's first monumental success muted to a warm hum of industriousness hovering just above the level of business as usual. I had proven myself as an idea man, and was encouraged to sit for nebulous hours in my window seat, drinking coffee and smoking cigarettes, waiting in my control-tower environment to guide the next planeload of concepts to a safe landing in my lap.

It was my habit to sit at home in the evenings, doing much as I did at work, smoking cigarettes and looking for ideas in the shapes of the smoke I exhaled. It was late spring and there were still no women in my life, but millions of them in my thoughts; the millions were, in all honesty, a rainbow of one. At home I was also given to staring from my windows, transfixed by a certain attitude that crept into my own reflection, as if I were awaiting the next decisive step of the actor at the center of the only drama to which I could relate. When an obstreperous neighbor lodged an unwarranted complaint with our unit manager about my so-called "peeping," I was asked politely to close my blinds at night ("Just to keep the old bat quiet," my landlord urged) and, obliging, I was forced back upon five looted rooms still charged with Paige's voice and memory. I had heard through the grapevine that Paige had enrolled at the university where she worked, and there was once again pursuing the M.A. she had previously abandoned to support my fledgling career. M.A.: those two letters embodied everything that I was able to learn about her, and I must admit that I did my share of obsessing over them.

More to pulverize the quietude of our apartment with sound than out of any genuine thirst for entertainment, I turned to television, zapping from one channel to another, until my hectic mood was calmed by a voice as soothing and neutral as a hypnotist's. . . .

Look at that technique, will you? Real Old World craftsmanship. You just don't see that anymore—unless you're tuned right here to TMN, the TeleMall Network. And we're offering this Old World craftsmanship to you this evening at an Old World price.

The roundheaded man on the screen was impeccably well dressed, like some of the more ambitious men in my own office, clean cut as if his grandfather's grooming tips had been the most head-turning information he'd ever tapped into his life-style. In the pinch of his thumb and index finger he held from its hook a single 14K "sunburst dangle" earring, imported from Spain. To the right of this composition, framed with a seemingly reasonable price and an 800 number, a digital clock counted down the seconds to zero. Flipping through sixty channels I found the same broadcast on no fewer than four channels in a gridlock of long-form infomercials and star-studded endorsements for life-skills instructors. I pressed on until I was halted, midzap, by a full-screen image of a woman's bare neck in profile, fetchingly adorned, rotating as if on a motorized pedestal toward its anterior profile.

. . . and the expansive white-gold webbing of this Bridgeford Garr design, you housewives out there, is the perfect camouflage for that dress in your closet that you feel is maybe cut just a bit too low. Again, the price of this necklace is down from $89.95; tonight, it can be yours for only $54.95. Now let's move up to the beautiful earrings Jill is wearing. Again, these are also from the Bridgeford Garr Collection—a TMN Exclusive—featuring the delicate but durable design for which Bridgeford Garr is world renowned. These are filigreed sterling with lapis cabochon, a royal combination to say the least. For you ladies with blue eyes, these stones will make them look that much deeper—ask anyone with our lapis accessories. See the way the studio lights here are playing off the edges of the stone cuttings? These are guaranteed to dazzle the eye, ladies, of any admirer.

I couldn't believe that I had freely accessed such pornography; I had turned no "Adults Only" key in my cable box, nor had I phoned a covert pay-per-view order into one of the blue channels. I told myself that, at such a late hour, broadcasters could probably get away with virtually anything. The proof was before my eyes. The unblinking focus on the neck and throat of the model at hand I found absolutely absorbing, the quality of the video feed so deliriously sharp that it could only be a live signal, richer in resolution and immediacy than professional one-inch videotape. I could make out the buff-strokes of the woman's television makeup, where it was applied in pats or in swirls like the stars of a van Gogh night; I could see the blond down of her nape, feathering up from her scruff and giving lie to the jet bottled black of her fashionably short haircut, the black better to offset the costly gleam of her bargain baubles.

Fun and fancy, this shoulder-duster design carries a single two-karat Diamonette stud. Maybe you're a suitor on the lookout for that lady who's just starting a Diamonette collection, a spouse with an important anniversary on the horizon, or perhaps you're a devoted son looking for that special Mother's Day gift. The entire design weighs out at eleven-K. That's not heavy, ladies . . . just grand. Let me ask the lovely Karen: Are those comfortable on you? They are? Well, they look like you were born with them, that's how nice they look from where I'm sitting.

There was an aspect to the presentation of these models, the plotless, rapid-fire replacement of one "type" with another, their reduction into identical, interchangeable, cropped details, that almost made me feel as if I was intercepting an underground telecast of *Throat Sprockets*. The camera hovered adoringly over provocative patches of pink and pigment, fleshscapes shading into soft valleys, limned ridges, all covered evenly as if by shallow snowdrifts of beige and brown, virgin territory waiting patiently to be run through, wrecked and ravished.

In a matter of moments the TeleMall Network moved on to "Concepts for Home Convenience," leaving me in a state of excitation bordering on panic. Why had I never noticed this flesh parade before? I grabbed my *TV Guide* and, finding TMN's programming itemized nowhere, jotted a reminder to myself in its margins of the channels that carried this broadcast, and the hour when the "Earrings and Necklaces" segment began.

• • •

The next night I began to record "Earrings and Necklaces." TMN devoted thirty minutes each weeknight to the segment, which meant that I was able to accommodate almost an entire week's worth of unduplicated modelings on a single VHS high-grade cassette.

And now here's Daisy, looking good in a style that, while it's very—I guess you could call it abstract—but remember, abstracts get hung in museums and you know why? That's right: because they last. And you can hang these right from your own two ears. And please note, "Pierced Only" on these. . . .

Youthful and *contemporary* are words that spring to mind when I see this provocative design from Taylor and Estes. As you see, these are ribbed hoops with a stunning patina effect lining each ridge. Absolutely beautiful. These have a snap-bar closure, making them very snug, perfect for dancing. Give your head a good shake, would you, Chelsea? Harder, harder! Atta girl. As I say, very young, very practical, but no reason why they wouldn't be just as appropriate a fashion accessory at a neighborhood bridge game for you more mature ladies.

This alluring pendant style earring from Pucci of Milan features a classic starburst configuration, extremely lightweight. It doesn't drag the earlobe down like some of your more audacious pendant designs. And, yes, those are diamonettes that you see outlining the corona around the hand-painted core. And would you believe it? The core has been painted differently on each pair of these one-of-a-kind beauties by internationally acclaimed artist Flavio Pucci. I don't know if you can see it on your TV, but these stones are cut in such a way that they actually cast out a scintillating rainbow effect that—well, at least here in the studio—! Very impressive. And this combination bargain and instant heirloom can be yours at the special TMN price of only $179.95. Or, if you prefer, for $45.00 a month for four months, using our convenient TMN Plan.

At times I would turn down the volume and improvise my own running commentary:

This blue topaz chandelier is perfect for stringing the high-held bow of Jill's jugulum.

Available in white or yellow gold, this lacy chain confection from Bristol & Bum lends a decorative rhyme to the delicate fretwork of Annalee's anterior ligaments.

These teardrop diamonettes, caught in a stylized clutch of sterling silver claws, provide an ideal cap to the exocervix of our Eileen.

In the weeks that followed, videocassettes began to line my living room shelves evicting, one by one, the books that reminded me of Paige and bedtimes past. As if to defuse the true seriousness with which I regarded my expanding menagerie, I used a labeling program at work to create professional-looking embossments for these homemade compilations. I recorded each of them with the sound levels at zero, allowing me to persist in imagining my own presentations of these skin-swathed objets d'art:

> There is much to admire in this black-bedded pearl garniture, particularly the way it highlights Cheryl's bonnet string muscle, like a tusk submerged in caramel, forking lissomely about the tempting bulge of a sunken peachstone.

Alas, before I had indulged myself to the extent of replacing an entire shelf of dusty books with factory-fresh cassettes, the TeleMall Network surprised me one night by dispensing altogether with its live models. Instead their diamonette junk was displayed on necklace stumps and velvet-covered earring trees— stemlike standees branching out into inverted commas, as if conscious of the *double entendre* of their appeal. I phoned the 800 number on the screen to voice my complaint, and an operator with a southern accent confided to me that, in recent weeks, TMN had been receiving more proposals of marriage during "Earrings and Necklaces" than actual orders.

At least I had my private collection.

I watched it compulsively, obsessively, using its images as a path toward a deeper understanding of the cigarettes that were so comforting to hold in my mouth. After enough cigarettes, I considered, my own apartment smelled like an ethereal annex to the smoking section in the House of Usherettes, or to that smoky room at the Chicago LaRonde. Cigarettes, I realized, are a habit we acquire from those phantoms of life from whom we desire everything but glean nothing else; they are the candles we light as shrines to the phantoms and ciphers and demons who enter our lives briefly and only to upset us, a contemplation in their honor. In terms of their ability to re-create the atmosphere of specific past moments, cigarettes are—after the cinema—the closest thing man has invented to a time machine.

I didn't realize it at the time, but these thoughts—another consequence of my exposure to *Throat Sprockets*—were girding me for another important campaign.

• • •

Barry Castleman and I talked one afternoon around the water-cooler about our experiences with home video. He surprised me by claiming to have in his personal collection a number of films that had not yet been legitimately released on tape, including one or two which, at that time, were not yet in theaters. I *know:* my mind raced to the same conclusion. . . .

I hesitated to ask him too much about these acquisitions, afraid it might scare him off and spoil my chances of using his connection for my own purposes, but Barry was a gregarious sort and I felt he might share the wealth if I could only keep him talking long enough. The longer we whispered beside the watercooler, the more he steered our conversation toward prurient descriptions of the highlights of certain porn tapes he adored—starring actresses with names like Caren Grant and Johanna Wayne, directed by Triple-X pioneers like Cecily DeMille—but he was discouraged from speaking very long about these matters by a sudden rush on the water supply by would-be eavesdroppers. Even Myla Monteith hovered at the tap, slowly filling a paper cup as we stood by, saying nothing, until she had taken it back to her office to pour on her potted cactus.

"Listen, I wouldn't want to get you or your contact in trouble," I murmured, "but there *is* a little something I'd like to find. If you feel funny about sharing his name, I understand, but maybe you could ask him if he has it, and if he does, you could order it for me?"

"I'll tell you what," Barry offered, looking over his shoulder at a sound he hadn't heard, "let me give this fellow a call and see if I can put you two together."

"Sounds good."

"That way, you see, I'm not personally involved in the transaction, which is as it should be. It might impede your freedom of choice, if I'm placing your orders for you, right? I mean, if you're looking for a movie about sheep, you probably wouldn't want a bigmouth like me knowing about it." Barry slapped my arm fraternally, to let me know that he was only joking, but still making a point.

At the end of the day I returned from the executive washroom to my office to find a calling card on the sill of my window seat. The name *Paul Hood* and a West Coast telephone number were scratched on one side. On the other side of the card was a note in Barry's most enthusiastic script: *This guy can find ANYTHING!!!*

• • •

Paul Hood answered his telephone plainly, like a man who did not waste time on ceremony or mind being identified with his service: "Hood's Got the Goods."

I gave him the name of the customer who had referred me, "Barry Castleman" functioning as my password into this entertainment netherworld. "There's something I've been looking for," I said in conclusion.

"Everybody's looking for something," Hood philosophized. "Does this masterpiece have a name?"

"*Throat Sprockets.*"

"The old Linda Lovelace thing? *No problema.*"

"*No comprendo,* you mean. Not *Deep Throat*—*Throat Sprockets.*"

"Okay then, what's it about?" Then, as if he sensed my reticence to be descriptive, he added: "Or doesn't it have an 'about'?"

"There's not much of a plot," I told him. "But it *has* an 'about.' "

"So tell me! I'm not here to slap your hand, pal."

"The title isn't enough for you to go on?"

"Not really."

"I can't say I'm surprised. There wasn't a title on the film itself, not on the print I saw, at any rate. I also saw it once in Chicago under the title *Transylvania Mon Amour.* I'm not even sure that *Throat Sprockets* is the real title, come to think of it."

"Ah—*untitleds*," Hood said, his gruff voice warming with enriched understanding. "Now we're getting somewhere."

"You say 'untitleds' like it's a genre unto itself."

"What's zat?"

"*Genre*," I clarified. "A type or category of film."

There was a vaguely insulting pause on his end. "So," he spoke up, "are you gonna tell me something more about this picture, or what?"

"I don't think I—"

"Look, primrose, don't waste my time! I get hundreds of calls a day, and if it ain't buyers, it's dealers, so you're costing me hard either way, you got that? So cough it out or hang the fuck up, okay?"

"I'm sorry, it's just that I don't know how to describe—"

"Is it one of those mammary movies? Or maybe something outta Kiddie City? Or one o' them blue erotic animal jobs? C'mon, c'mon, c'mon! Gimme a hand here, I'm not Jeane Dixon, you know! Am I getting warm at least? Or is *cold* meat what you're after?"

There was a pause, during which the temperature on Hood's end seemed to drop twenty full degrees, inviting me to ponder what lay beyond the extremities of animal cruelty and murder for entertainment.

"Wait a minute—who did you say gave you my number?"

"Barry Castleman? Friendship, Ohio?"

"How did *he* get my number?"

"Don't sweat it," I said. "I'm not looking for snuff pictures."

"Are you a cop?" he asked.

"No."

"Then I know," he said, his voice suddenly an octave lower with sudden tension. "I think I know what you're looking for, but you're too late. I know what you're looking for, you want the one with what's-her-name. Right, the TV actress? You know the one, the one who got canned from that big show, oh, about five or six years back?"

"*Throat Sprockets* isn't a made-for-TV movie," I assured him, "believe me."

"You know what I mean. Don't you go getting smart. You know, you know the one, the one I'm talking about with the pretty hair, the Irish, the creamy Irish bitch? Never heard from again, am I right? Well, pal, she isn't out West doing auditions, let me tell you. She ain't out there dancin' up the Walk of Fame with Mr. Spoons. I'll tell you who she danced with. 'Cause I got it on half-inch, muthafucka!"

The videocassette that Hood proceeded to describe was not *Throat Sprockets;* I knew this much from his first gutter adjective. Nevertheless I was compelled to hear him out, hoping somewhere in my heart that his words might blast me out of the corner into which *Throat Sprockets* had painted me, even if it meant risking the knowledge of darker distractions.

"I don't remember her name, but you'll remember it as soon as you see her. Nice tits, but they're always out of focus 'cause the camera is looking lower down. It's *lowdown,* man. She's a pink one, peeled right down to her bikini wax, nothing left to the imagination, the works. It's like they say; watching this tape is like looking at some sick fuck's dream, you know, because it's like you know this girl somehow, but then again you don't. Once the dream gets going, it starts turning bad and you start thinking that maybe you should just say to hell with this headache and eject the damn thing but somehow you just can't, you know? You know what that's like, right? Right? I know you're still there, man; I can hear you jerkin' off. . . .

"Well, there they are, bouncin' the mounds 'n shakin' the bacon —but, just as the guy starts to come, he starts, I dunno, vibrating or something. He vibrates till you can't even get a clear view of his outline, you know what I'm sayin', and then he's like turning red and it's like, 'What the—?' It's like he's burning up with some kind of fever, and his shoulder blades start beatin' up and down like a butterfly's, hummin' red like some friggin' race car and then . . . Aw, Jesus, man. . . ."

"And then what?"

"Jesus, Jesus Christ," Hood testified, his voice hoarse with a fund of emotion, "this guy with her, when he stops vibratin', you're lookin'—" Precipitous silence. Abyss.

"Hood?"

He whispered, as if not wanting to be overheard: "He turns around, like he's suddenly aware that he's being watched. And when he turns around, you're lookin' at—it's the *Devil* Himself. . . ."

"You mean there's a dissolve," I reasoned. "That's an old eight-millimeter-reel gag from way back. Having a man go up in a puff of smoke, replaced by an actor in horns with a pitchfork. Méliès invented it."

"That's. Not. What. I'm. Saying, you stupid shit."

"I don't—"

"I'm not saying that. At all."

"Come on, you don't expect me to believe that—"

"I'll send it to you. You watch it, just watch a little bit, and you'll see. I gotta warn you, though, I didn't tell you everything. It's—hard to tell everything."

"There's more?"

"I think so. When I saw that red and hairy thing start to turn around, it was like it had sensed my presence. It was a recording, I know, but I felt a sense of imminent danger, like if it turned all the way around and faced the camera, that it would be able to see me. And that if it knew me by sight, it could find me. I didn't want to risk that, so I erased the rest. Everything but the sex part and the beginning of the, you know—"

"Transformation?"

"Whatever," Hood said flatly, recovering his guard. "Doesn't sound like your *Throat Sprocket,* huh?"

"*Sprockets*," I corrected him. "No, thank God."

There was a short pause. "You're probably thinkin' I put all the money I make up my nose, ain'tcha?"

"It's really none of my concern what you do with your money or your nose, Mr. Hood."

"Just plain 'Hood'—that's the way I like it."

"Anything you say."

"Spoken like a man with a hard-on for a tape. Call me crazy, pal, but there are movies out there that can really fuck you up. Running a service like this is like being a pharmacist, you dig? My shelves are full of uncut videos, full-strength shit, and I've gotta make a judgment about how much is safe to prescribe to my customers. I could make a fortune with that tape—*you know*," he interrupted himself in a clandestine whisper, "*the one I just mentioned* —if it was complete, but I haven't regretted erasing it for a minute. Not for a second. You know why?"

"Tell me."

"All right, buy yourself a hat and keep this under it. After I erased that tape—you know which one—I remembered that I had sold a copy to this guy out near Lubbock. Those cowboys get lonesome, I guess, and he was lookin' for hard core on this actress, and heard I had a lot of Famous T & A in my collection. If people want Madonna and Warren Beatty, Sharon Tate and Romeo Polanski, even Marilyn and JFK, I may not have it on the shelf, but I guaran-fuckin'-tee you, I can get my hands on *anything*. If it ever happened, *somebody* has it on tape. Believe me, pal, I don't shit where I eat, you know what I'm sayin'?"

"Lubbock," I reminded him.

He was silent, as if either summoning the strength to go on, or questioning the wisdom of it. "Lubbock, Texas," he continued. "Well, I sold the tape before I'd had a chance to check it myself, right? I got dozens of thousands of tapes here and there ain't enough hours in my life. After I finally got done looking at it, first thing I did was to call that guy to warn him what was on the tape, to offer him a refund and get him to maybe send it back. I didn't even wait until morning. His telephone was answered by someone who said that this fella wasn't in and could I please leave my name. Well, fuck me, pal, but I wasn't born yesterday; I know the way cops talk. So I hung up before they could trace my ass.

"From what I heard later, this guy's wife found him in his den about two o'clock in the morning, his drawers pulled down round his ankles. She was so shocked, thinkin' she'd walked in on the poor bastard pullin' his pud, that she didn't notice right away . . . but his eyes had been completely burned out. But not really. Truth is, they had been burned *in*.

"Now," he concluded after a dramatic pause, sounding completely refreshed, "maybe you can tell me what wimpy little thing *you* want."

I described *Throat Sprockets* to him.

To my immense relief Hood knew the film. He had a copy in stock—with no title on the print—but he admitted that it wasn't in particularly good shape. *He'll pop Satan Himself into your VCR and turn your eyes to toast, but at least he's an honest businessman,* I thought. I told Hood that I expected any print of the film to be full of annoying edits and patches of missing footage, but he explained that he was speaking in terms of generational loss.

"The copy I sell you is a copy of a copy of somebody else's copy," he enumerated.

"Well," I suggested, "would it be possible for you to backtrack, to get a generation or two closer to the source tape, to make me a clearer copy? I could make it worth your while."

"You *couldn't* make it worth my while, pal. You don't know the kinds of people I have to deal with. I could let you have my original, that'd save you one generation, for five hundred dollars. Take it or leave it. I could get more for it, but I figure I can pass on savings to people who can keep secrets. You won't tell anybody about Blind Boy Lubbock, will you, buddy? Not that you could prove anything."

"What do you think?" I asked.

"What do *you* think?" he countered.

"I think you're probably not the sort of man who would kill a sale because a customer tells him he's full of shit."

"No, sir; I certainly am not."

"Sold to the man from Ohio for five hundred dollars."

• • •

"Paul doesn't exactly sound like an honors grad, does he?" Barry laughed, when I thanked him the next day for the contact. "Those tapes he watches have really screwed him up. I have an uncle Ed; the second World War did the same thing to him."

I put a $505 check in the mail to Paul Hood, adding the fiver to cover postage and handling. My phone bill arrived soon after, proving to me that our unreal conversation had in fact taken place. I spent a couple of lunch breaks at the main branch of the Friendship Library examining Lubbock newspapers from the past year on microfilm, merely out of curiosity, and in the back pages of a February edition found the relevant item. There was a small photo of a middle-aged man. I swallowed deeply and stared into his friendly photographed eyes—the future site of two mortal hollows.

How deep *is* the ocean?

• • •

Barry Castleman's wife decided to visit her family in Indianapolis that weekend, leaving him and me (as he put it) like "shipmates on the S.S. *Companionless.*" After work on Friday we dined together at Sarno's, spicing their veal parmigiana special with the latest office gossip. Dinner began with drinks and continued with drinks. Barry, though well beneath Myla Monteith on the corporate ladder, claimed during his third Wild Turkey to have once finger-fucked her in a between-floors elevator. We reiterated the ancient rumor of the Old Man's penile implant, and that about exhausted the skeleton content of any closets fitting our particular keys. I expressed sadness over a recent news item announcing that the Eros Theater had permanently closed, and Barry commented with a look through the window at the homebound Friday traffic that he'd never quite mustered the gumption to step inside that fading flesh-and-flea pit.

"You, who fucked Myla Monteith with your favorite finger?" I ironized.

"Yeah, well, my horoscope told me I could get away with that." He grinned, signaling to the bartender.

"What did your horoscope say about this weekend?"

He finished his drink in a swallow. "Not to talk to whores in Church. So no matter what, Church is out."

Somewhere between our third and fourth round two married revelers of Barry's acquaintance—Kirsten and somebody Fosseck —came roaring in like specters from the Speakeasy Era and joined us, packing our modest booth shoulder to shoulder, and ordered fresh ones all around. It wasn't long before I'd drunk enough Chivas to no longer give a righteous rut how openly I admired the bare throat of this Kirsten creature, whose blue eyes and Sassooned blond hair—cut to follow the line of her jaw— offset it so attractively. Her husband, discerning of my interest, surprised me by throwing her to the wolf.

"Dance with the man, Curse," he encouraged, as the jukebox tipped into a Jimmy Buffett number—not my type of dancing music at all, but neither was she my wife and SPLICE nor were we anymore in Sarno's, which I remembered had no jukebox, no dance floor; Barry and I had left Sarno's sometime earlier, on a southward Chivas breeze and an Austin Nichols crutch.

Another man would've taken advantage of the nearness of her perfect ear to whisper an invitation to a quiet cubicle in the men's room, but the question that actually arose to my lips asked if she was an Ohio girl. She looked at me as if she hadn't heard me correctly. My own drunken concern with the issue startled me. Her answer came hesitantly, like something too personal to be asked of a new acquaintance—particularly of one so hell-bent, to all appearances. Yes, she was.

"By the way," she said, "I suppose congratulations are in order."

"Why is that?" I wondered.

"The bibulous Barry Castleman said something about how your new car commercial is going in front of the cameras—out in Hollywood. Local boy makes good."

"That already happened," I said, thinking, *Hood's Got the Goods.* In time I added, "I wasn't invited to the shoot."

"Oh? Why not?"

"The director was some European hotshot. Had his own concepts about my concepts."

She rested her head on my shoulder; it had the gentle weight of commiseration. Holding a different woman in my arms—a different Ohio woman—felt disorienting, a familiarity deranged, a role performed by an understudy. This was no globe-trotting gal more laid over than laid in Chicago, but a local woman who might have once been in line to be my wife, lover, neighbor, or co-worker, and—whoa, pretty nelly! I had to put this baby down while I was still sober enough to deny my instincts. Fortunately, Castleman saved me the embarrassment by cutting in after the second chorus—"Watch out for this boy's fingernails," I warned her in parting—and I stumbled back among the tilt-a-whirl tables of spectators. I watched as the bibulous Barry Castleman molded Kirsten to him, following the diagrams of experience as the dance floor shrank to a single tile, supporting only the two of them.

Where the hell was I?

The parking lot was no more stable, as we ran uphill: the sodden wreckage of Barry Castleman, the married couple my senses told me were adventuring for a third partner, and that little old piss-a-minute procrastinator, me. Our alcoholic vision scouted around the crowded gravel emptiness for their car.

"All right," Barry hollered, "where's Kirsten's vulva?"

"Volvo," she corrected him with a growling, half-shocked laugh. "Honestly, Barry!" She looked at me intently, as if Barry had mentioned something she hoped I was thinking of, to see if there was any sign of blush or thirst in my expression. Kirsten Fosseck's glance held firm until Barry and her nameless, incoherent husband had climbed inside her car. I climbed into the backseat beside Barry, who had become surprisingly withdrawn in his cups.

Four or five blocks away, while pausing under a stoplight, Barry tugged softly at my shirtsleeve, so softly it might have been an errant breeze, but it was an unseasonably cold night for May and our windows weren't rolled down . . . which was exactly Barry's point. He signaled weakly with the crook of a finger to lower my window, which I did, needing some air myself. Barry scrambled in slow motion across my lap to the window, leaned out, and hurled copious amounts of ferment custard into the gutter.

I had never seen a man miss his wife so much.

By the time we pulled in front of my apartment complex, it was well after two o'clock. The husband riding shotgun was sleeping sonorously, and Kirsten turned around in her driver's seat to face me, allowing the engine to idle. I thrilled that the sound might concern my conservative neighbors, bring one or two jealous faces to their windows.

"Why don't I get these two home," she said, soft words lending an urgency to her hard blue eyes, "and then maybe double back . . . ?"

Something inside me, without hesitation, said no. "I appreciate that, Kirsten, but listen: I'm bad news. I'm the obituary page, to tell you the God's honest truth."

She stared at me, perhaps half stimulated by my pronouncement, but thoroughly uncertain of whether it was hyperbole to deflect her attentions or the true report of a loaded gun. I'm not sure why I said what I did; it came from a sense that something wasn't right, a conviction that this was not a caravan I should climb aboard.

I shook Kirsten's hand, listening to the clink of her shaken bracelet and the sound of her name in my mouth, and hugged my pillow tightly as I took both memories to bed with me.

What Barry and I had survived that evening felt enormous and significant, but shrank to plainest shame in the following weeks under the office track-lighting. Black Friday was an evening neither of us wished to remember; thereafter, whenever we bumped into each other at work, Barry's deflective expression awoke memories of me holding his stomach, seeing him vomit from a place so deep inside that it had never found a voice, and knowing the reason why.

• • •

The next morning a padded envelope bearing a Santa Barbara postmark appeared on my doorstep. Inside were *two* cassettes.

DEMOLISHED

OST FILMS ARE MADE TO BE SEEN AND KNOWN ENTIRELY AT FIRST glance; they also tend to evaporate from our minds on the first pass. Any film worth knowing deserves to be known well, to be seen more than once, but the very best films tend to seduce us with a virtual reality that begs to be escaped into, perhaps once per year, for the rest of our lives. Favorite films should be cherished, their towns revisited, their characters met and loved and lost all over again, their stories replayed to the point of assimilation—like a favorite record, a pet trauma, or a good stretch of road.

In a sense *Throat Sprockets* was both types of film. I truly believe that it revealed itself to me completely, in all its dimensions and subtexts, on first viewing; it was love at first sight. Its depth of penetration into my psyche had also made it possible for me to revisit the film so vividly in memory that my own memory of the film had become a kind of *virtual sexuality*. While fishing through my subconscious for ideas at work, while riding home on the Metro, and during "Earrings and Necklaces" marathons—my memory of *Throat Sprockets* had knocked down the walls of the old me, and built a new wing onto my house of experience—a disturbing extension of raised ceilings and sunken rooms.

Today, of course, everything we might possibly want to know about *Throat Sprockets* is (or was) catalogued, but in those days it was left to us to assemble for ourselves a form of light from the random shards of darkness we could find. The bootleg videocassette of *Throat Sprockets* that arrived from Santa Barbara was itself only a fragment; it appeared to be complete but, as Hood had warned, it was several generations removed from its original source, and its fuzzy picture quality was less reliable in many ways than my own mental retention of its images and narration. I suspected that Hood had taken the money I had paid for his own copy and sent me a cheap reproduction. The generational flaws were nevertheless informative: I could see enough of the film to tell it had been struck from the same print shown at the Eros—all of the splices were exactly as I had seen them before, and both the massage and hotel scenes were missing. In essence what I had paid for was the evidence of the cassette's poor image resolution, which persuasively testified to the fact that I wasn't the only collector with an interest in this particular film. Despite its flaws I watched the tape often, if only to remind myself that I wasn't alone. We were still underground then, like seeds.

Seeing the immense theatrical image compressed to video dimensions for the first time gave me a mistaken sense of mastery over the film. Whereas it had once absorbed me, so now could I absorb it. I let the four other rooms of my apartment go to hell, dust gathering on surfaces and dishes stacking in and around my sink, as I set about a thorough examination of this new wing from my living room. The murkiness of Hood's tape forced me to concentrate on its images with more aggression than was sensible or comfortable. After each viewing I rewound the cassette in a state of mental exhaustion and smoked a joint to relieve the optic pressure. My head would pound as I recounted that, when the indigo choker was held suspended between the Glover's hands at the film's end, the fleshtone beads might have formed any words at all, or merely a design. Had I really, at one time, seen THE END printed upon that necklace? How could this have been, when my relationship with this film, *with that scene,* had been only just beginning? A headful of questions and a handful of aspirin later, I pressed Play again.

• • •

After renewing my acquaintance with *Throat Sprockets* one of the first things I did was place calls to the information outlets of all the major cities in North America, requesting the number of Lotus Films. Why hadn't I tried this before? I didn't honestly expect to find their office in the most obvious metropolitan headquarters of motion-picture production and distribution, but my hopes grew as I began dialing the area codes of more probable places like Seattle and Boston. My excitement reached its peak when, one sleepless night, it occurred to me to check the business pages of Friendship's own telephone directory. Alas, there was no such listing to be found, nor did I find any recordings of recent disconnections.

Next I tried to chart the duration of each scene by stopwatch, searching for numerical patterns in the film's placement of splices. There was no apparent scheme, but neither was I able to chart the film in its entirety; no matter how familiar I was with the picture, there was always some arresting image—for instance, the Glover's hand reaching out to caress a woman's throat, to hoist her kiss to his lips, as if she were a goblet from which to drink—that helped me to forget the higher intentions of mathematics, then another image, more shocking, and another, that dropped the stopwatch from my hand.

Only one aspect of *Throat Sprockets* remained undiminished on Hood's bootlegged cassette. Shakespeare's Dark Lady, the nameless brunette presented with the beaded choker at the end—the consolidation of all the nameless objectified women who preceded her—haunted me more than ever with her troubled, downcast stare. There was an unspoken burden about her, visible even through the fuzziness of Hood's bad transfer, a burden that I found myself yearning to define and share or assume. Sometimes, while playing my cassette, I paused on her face, freezing the best available frame, and held a magnifying glass to the screen, looking between the stacked resolution lines for clues to her surroundings, places where I might find her in the real world—the world, after all, where *Throat Sprockets* had been filmed—reflected in her eyes. The most I ever found dwelling there was the much clearer reflection of my own haunted face looking back at me.

• • •

After a month or two of almost constant use Hood's videocassette was eaten by my VCR. It was regurgitated by my deck in an endless black choker of unspooling tape, and there was no means of salvaging it. It was history. I called Barry Castleman to get Paul Hood's number, which I had misplaced. In a distracted voice that implied a still-thriving embarrassment over our night on the town last spring, Barry advised me not to call. Hood's operation had been busted by the FBI, and his underground video empire was now kaput. It wouldn't be kaput forever, I reflected, because I was still in possession of his most incriminating evidence. I had never summoned the nerve to pop in that second cassette, the one Hood had labeled *Blind Boy Lubbock*. After staring at its unopened plastic casing for the better part of an hour, the angel won and I took that gratis tape straight to my building's incinerator.

For the time being, there was no road back to *Throat Sprockets*. And so came the dry spell before the deluge.

• • •

Something that concerned me, throughout the following weeks of separation, was the nagging sense that I had glimpsed *Throat Sprockets'* Dark Lady in the periphery of other films, like a ghost haunting the rear rooms of other mansions.

My life would go on, and just as I arrived at the point of forgetting her, I would see her dark, shoulder-length hair and square jaw trudging purposefully along in a crowd of Manhattan pedestrians lending scenery to an argument between Sigourney Weaver and Harrison Ford . . . or accidentally reflected in a full-length mirror being fought over in an antique store by the romance-bound Gérard Depardieu and Andie MacDowell, which, during their tug-of-war, happened to flash a glimpse of the crouching production crew (was this where she had disappeared —*behind* the camera?) . . . or standing with her back to the camera as a sobbing woman being comforted by twin sister Jodie Foster, who resembled my Dark Lady only from behind. Of course, I would never have seen such mainstream films had the Eros not kept its date that summer with the wrecker's ball.

A month or so before the date of demolition I attended a sale of Eros artifacts held by the Chamber of Commerce, passing through those familiar portals for the last time. The Titian-haired cashier and the usher's Brylcreem-and-talc bouquet had fled into the theater's past with Tyrone Power; I had survived these things. The bronze peelings from the dome above the lobby had been swept from the main path into corners, where they were piled like rakings from an autumn wood where everything had turned to gold or shrapnel. What was most disorienting in the midst of so much decay, however, was that the Eros bustled that afternoon with so much life; the covert atmosphere of its open-for-business hours was supplanted with loud bartering, merriment, and laughter. I saw middle-aged women—who had been romanced there during *Meet Me in St. Louis* in the forties, *Teacher's Pet* in the fifties, and *Camelot* in the sixties—walking out with souvenir lamps and ashtrays and adding machines, or walking with a victorious air behind packs of movers carrying dust-matted antique desks and chairs to suburban destinations. I saw one especially happy-looking fellow with his eye on the popcorn machine; I did my civic duty and warned him that it was only a prop, that the Eros had sold only prepopped corn bought in enormous transparent sacks, and for my effort was told to fuck off.

Perhaps it was the absence of the theater staff, but the sense of liberation I felt in the Eros that afternoon was both heady and dreamlike. No velvet rope barred the balcony from popular access (pity the poor soul who bought the velvet drapes!); I could move in any direction I chose. I grabbed that last chance and climbed the stairs into the long-forbidden balcony. Halfway up the flight, set within an enormous wall, was an imposing mosaic mural depicting an old-fashioned Hollywood premiere. Distance lent enchantment; some of the color patches, I could see up close, were missing. *Were the mosaics being sold by the piece?* I wondered.

I moved on, admiring the ornate golden banister, comfortable and reassuring to my hand, which followed the curvature of the stairwell into the sagging mezzanine, so perfectly fitted that it could serve no other practical purpose and would likely perish there with the rest of the architecture, its dogtooth moldings and fan tracery and pudgy, cackling Cupids. Downstairs, a chandelier had been purchased and was being lowered into light that exposed the shame of its heavy webbings. The balcony, when I reached it, was dark and musty but it afforded an excellent view of the screen and main floor. Every vanilla cushion had been quietly returned to its rightful place; the overturned table was upright again. Most of the old, dirty, corduroy-lined seats below had disappeared, unbolted from the floor, exchanged for cash, and dragged out into the modern sunlight. As I turned to leave, a cockroach skittered across a seatback limned by the golden light filtering in from the mezzanine. I had a sense that I was surrounded by them.

I also toured the subterranean vaults, where the steel doors and marbled surfaces struck me with an (under the circumstances) absurd sense of permanence; the Spartan dressing rooms backstage, where George Burns and Mickey Rooney (sorry—make that *Joe Yule, Jr.*) had once upon a decade made themselves presentably vaudevillian; and, in a walk-in closet situated within yelling distance of the downstairs offices (where I glimpsed an old bifocaled gentleman in suspenders, sucking an unlighted cigar stub), I rummaged through bales and bales of twine-bound one-sheet posters, dating back thirty years or more. I spent more than an hour rifling through them, souvenirs of everything the Eros had played throughout the length of my life, but the *Throat Sprockets* poster was not among them. I decided to take a *Blue Hawaii* poster as a small consolation prize, as well as a seat plucked from approximately my position in the Eros on that night when my life forever changed, whose dark corduroy surface the sunlight revealed as a black-grooved burgundy.

It was not long after the sale that I stood in a crowd of hundreds of brown-bagging spectators to watch a wrecking ball slam the Eros into submission like one of its own latter-day starlets. Slam: pigeons fled from her plastered alcoves like bursts of flapping paper into the summer sky. *Those balls aren't shooting blanks*, I thought to myself. I studied the crowd and figured that one in five businessmen watching the death of the old movie palace had, at one time or another, been inside her and was experiencing thoughts similar to my own. Here we were again, staring at pictures provided us by her; again they gave us no pleasure, just a peculiar anxiety that felt like pleasure, the anxiety that resides *under* pleasure. The city's Queen died a whore, whorls of vermin aborting from her womb underground, as heavy clouds of dust and powdered granite settled on the Jazz Age Davids strewn in dismantled dignity throughout her court.

Afterward I finished my lunch in the third row of the Elite. A modest screening room of a theater, the Elite had a seating capacity of only 168 (a number framed on a white card outside the door by the fire department) but that afternoon held only myself and another customer seated a few rows from the back. There I watched, and he slept through, *My Fair Hooker* (at least that's what it should have been called), an overbudgeted trifle starring one of the most grating actresses I had ever seen. That evening on television I saw that woman described by a magazine commercial as one of the year's most intriguing people, and I heard the film that I had seen in an all-but-empty theater described as a mega-block-buster.

Before the year was out the Elite also closed. Downtown Friendship was left without a single movie theater to call its own. Deprived of theaters to contain it, fantasy had no recourse but to spill over into the city streets.

3

Said to her: "I have got a shocking sight in my head. Take it out." Her pleasing vivacity did remove it.

James Boswell
Journals

RELEASED

A CITY WITHOUT THEATERS IS A GUILTY CITY; IT IS A PLACE WHERE DREAMS have become too terrible to share, not least of all in darkness, among strangers caught in the vortex of the same material. The autumn closing of the Elite was met with an editorial from our local newspaper, which formally regretted the closing of Friendship's last downtown theater where, not so long ago, reserved-seat engagements had played to standing-room-only crowds; even more regrettable, it claimed, were the Elite's last tawdry years of existence: a tiny box where third-run stereo prints played in monophonic sound, barely in focus, to room only.

The Old Man brought the editorial to my attention. By this time Austin was used to finding me poised in a glazed, contemplative attitude on the window seat of my office, staring outside as if transfixed by some strength-sapping program, sometimes noting that I looked like I'd been watching television for two weeks. (He had no *idea*.) More recently, he had strolled past my open door and, glimpsing me in the same spot, tuned to the same panorama, remarked, "Tell me, do you ever wish you could change the channel?" (He had no *idea*.)

After he had continued on his constitutional rounds, I found myself wondering whether the Old Man, by suggesting my changing the channel of my picture window, was in fact planting the suggestion of transferring me to another town. Rumors had been circulating for a while that Sutton Perry & Ingersoll would be opening branch offices in Manhattan and Los Angeles, though Austin—eccentric that he was—was said to be resolute in his determination to keep Friendship, Ohio, as the agency's home base. Most of us who whispered about this possibility assumed that Nate Wechsel, who had family in upstate New York, would almost certainly be given charge of the East Coast office; I, on the other hand, knew better than to assume anything where Austin Ingersoll was concerned. I was not particularly keen on moving, or being moved, to either of those locations; there was enough stress in my private life without relocating to New York City, and my grip on reality was already so tenuous that I might go completely mad living in Hollywood, finding myself surrounded by the three-dimensional, flesh-and-blood forms of stars I recognized from two-dimensional films and television.

I sat in my window seat and imagined myself Out There, bumping into the real Pamela Franklin or Joan Blackman at the local market, driving daily past the bungalow where John Belushi overdosed and getting caught in traffic amid limousines with windows as black as the eyes of sharks, entrusting my legal affairs to Bela Lugosi, Jr. These would represent dangerously potent changes in the texture of life for someone as unsettled as me, and now they might easily happen. These were the thoughts before me when the Old Man rapped on my door, bringing the Elite story to my attention.

The Elite, like the Eros, was gone but home video—the columnist proselytized—would survive these dinosaurs in perfectly good stead. Home video was always in focus and there were no talking patrons to drown out the dialogue, nor were there spilled fountain drinks to Dentu-creme your shoes to a sloping floor.

"When I read that," Austin said, "I thought immediately of you . . . and the TV Heaven campaign."

"What, *Myla's* account?"

"TV Heaven is the client of Sutton Perry & Ingersoll," I was corrected, "and Myla has let it be known that she will be taking an indefinite leave of absence from said company, effective as of November fifteenth." A little less than two weeks away.

"I see," I said gravely. "Nothing wrong, I hope."

"I can't speak for her; you understand."

"Sure. Of course not."

"Anyway, I read this . . . *eulogy* and thought of you. I thought I'd offer you the chance to prove I wasn't wrong."

I rose to the occasion, leaving my window seat to pace industriously up and down the carpeted path behind my desk. "Okay," I began, always a good incantation. "This is how I see it. Average guy—right?—goes out to the movies, looking for a little escapism. As soon as he sits down, people start talking. His shoes stick to the floor. A big lady in an even bigger hat sits down right in front, a nightmare of plumage and cellulite. Movie comes on."

"Movie comes on . . . *good.*"

My life would go on and, just as I arrived at the point of forgetting her . . .

"And this beautiful girl appears on the screen . . . but she's all out of focus."

"Beautiful girl . . . *beautiful.*"

"Our Guy pulls his hair out and runs screaming up the aisle. (We should undercrank that shot, don't you think?) Okay. Then we cut to outside. Get this, Austin: Our Guy pulls up to the theater driving a wrecker's ball rig! Oh, God, I can *see* this! He swings it hard, knocks the fucker down. Insert time-lapse construction shot of a TV Heaven store going up in its place!"

"Yes, I follow you," the Old Man purred. "Then we see Our Guy at home, later that night, popping a tape from TV Heaven into his VCR. And then . . . and then the zinger. We'll need a zinger here."

"How's this? We cut to his TV screen. On the TV the movie begins and it shows . . . what else? Our Guy sitting on his own living-room couch! But it's not in his living room—it's on a *cloud!* And the babe, the one who was out of focus before? She's not only in focus—she brings him a can of beer and sits on his lap! And for the tag? The girl drapes her arms around Our Guy and he sighs, 'They Don't Call It TV Heaven For Nothin'!' "

Austin was smiling to himself, but I sensed a hesitancy over something moot. "Beer, I don't know," he finally said, "this isn't a beer commercial."

"Okay then, no beer." A cardinal rule of advertising: Always include a flaw in your design for the boss to correct.

He brooded, pacing a smaller path than my own. "There might also be charges of sexism," he projected.

"So milk it. That kind of thing could land us a couple of cover stories, minimum, on *Entertainment Tonight.* If she's in a bikini, maybe three."

"Of course, a lot, too, will depend on the actor," he hedged, "but . . ." The sly, inward smile went public. "I *like* it."

He rolled up the newspaper and swatted me with it.

On the way out the door Austin turned around and started breaking up. "That's right"—he laughed—"he's going to a *beach* movie!"

• • •

My first impulse was only a few slight embellishments away from the television and print ads that finally replaced TV Heaven's previous campaign. While filming commenced on a closed Hollywood set with Danny DeVito, I sat in my Ohio apartment, undressed and unshaven, sucking on a magnum of champagne, and occupying myself with a TV Heaven catalogue that had tumbled through the mail slot.

TV Heaven differed from their competition by offering customers access to Japanese, Chinese, and Venezuelan imports that, unlike tapes from most other countries, shared the NTSC format of North American releases and therefore could be played on domestic equipment. It was in the midst of the import listings that I found a postage-stamp-sized reproduction of the *Throat Sprockets* poster, decorated in garish streaks of Japanese hyperbole. No English-language title was provided, but there was no mistaking it. I immediately picked up the phone and dialed the number on the catalogue, which belonged to a TV Heaven store on my daily Metro route, and used the catalogue number to order a VHS import of *Throat Sprockets*. After the sexy voice on the phone calculated my yen and what the damages would be, I was told to expect its arrival in approximately three weeks.

In fact, it was only a matter of days before I decided to visit TV Heaven on my way home, to check out their selection of compact discs. I needed some new voices to sing me to sleep. Inside, the walls were lined with thousands of rental tapes, each cassette in repose inside its own black plastic box. I was pleasantly surprised by the scope of their CD Opera section (obviously the indulgent work of an interested staffer), and knowing very little about opera on any kind of level, I allowed my choice to be guided as usual by the cover photo of the female soloist's throat. My attention was drawn to the exquisite strain of a note launched from a geisha's throat during a performance of *Madama Butterfly*, which had forced her bonnet-string muscle to the fore like a slim, pliable, subcutaneous tuning fork, when I happened to overhear the arrival of an import shipment. The store manager, a tall, pale fellow in a Siouxsie & the Banshees T-shirt, signed the carboned receipt on the UPS carrier's clipboard, then used a Swiss Army knife to cut through the threaded shipping tape that secured the contents of a medium-sized package. I moved closer to the counter and watched as he removed several import cassettes from their packing and stacked them, one by one, beside the cash register. I read their spines: *Tempest in a G-Spot* . . . *Happy Tampon*

. . . *Gun Crazy* . . . *Blow Up* . . . *New Sister's Underwear* 2 . . .
Throat Sprockets! It had arrived—two weeks earlier than expected!

I dropped the suddenly unimportant *Madama Butterfly* CD
among the recorded works of Lynyrd Skynyrd and approached
the counter. My heart pounding wildly, I felt exhilarated by the
good fortune of my visit, but also vexed by the possibility that
this early arrival did not belong to me, and emboldened with the
mad determination that it would be mine before I left the store. A
thousand questions fired through my brain at the sight of the
video-store cashier's turtleneck collar, which made the situation
even more daunting.

She, on the other hand, had only one question for me: "Can I
help you?"

"Yes, I believe this tape here"—I tapped the appropriate spine
in the stack—"is mine? I ordered it a while ago, and it's just dumb
luck that I happened to stop by this evening."

"Japanese import, eh?" She smiled knowingly. "Big spender."
She extracted *Throat Sprockets*, the wild card, from the deck and
typed some information into her computer. "*Throat Sprockets*," she
said aloud, elasticating each syllable across infinite plains of inter-
nal space. Two or three women customers in the store overheard
her and pivoted for a look at the type of man who would order
such a title; one of them slipped her arm protectively around her
young son, instinctively guiding him toward a colorful point-of-
purchase display for Walt Disney's *Cinderella*. It took considerable
willpower to restrain myself from accusing *Cinderella* out loud of
being singularly responsible for all the foot and shoe fetishism in
the world.

"*Throat Sprockets*—haven't seen that one yet," the cashier continued. Instinct told me that she probably wasn't angling for an
invitation either. "Sounds like it's really Out There. And you
are . . . ?"

The name she spoke was not mine, but I took it as my own for
the sake of argument.

She smiled and rang up my purchase, unable to resist repeated inquisitive glances at the box, a perfect reproduction of the original poster art. "So let's see now, $169.95 plus tax is . . ."

"Plastic," I said, producing my gold card from my wallet. "To each his own."

As the girl was preparing to run a call-check on my card, something stopped her cold. My name. My real name.

"Oh, wait," she said, handing my card back to me. "I'm sorry, sir. I must have misunderstood you. You see, this tape was ordered by somebody else several weeks ago. Wait a minute." Her hands clattered across her keyboard. "Yes," she murmured as understanding dawned. "You see, your order for this title was placed only a few days ago. I'm sorry."

"I see."

"Your copy isn't due to arrive for another few weeks yet."

"That's too bad. Gee, you know, I'd really like to have it. Seeing as how I'm already here and everything."

"I'm sorry, but I just can't let you have this copy." With a deft movement she placed the cassette under the counter where I could no longer be tempted to argue over it.

"C'mon, sure you can," I pressed.

One of the women customers led her son out of the store.

"Sure you can," I repeated, keeping my voice down. "Look, I've ordered lots of things—not just tapes—in my time, and I'm always being told *It hasn't come in yet, it hasn't come in yet.* Couldn't you tell this person, if he should call and ask, that the tape is on back order or something? And when my copy comes in, in a week or two, he can have that one! I mean, after all, he might not decide to pick this tape up for two or three weeks! Don't tell me that's never happened before. All this means is that he'll be coming in a little later than expected—*maybe*—and I won't have to make the extra trip all the way out here. On the bus."

The confusion in the girl's face was touching, which made the secrets underlying her turtleneck all the more stimulating.

"Is there a problem, Gail?" It was the store manager, coming to her rescue. The cashier, Gail, explained to him what I had proposed and he, perhaps recognizing the potential for violence in my resolve, waved an arm and said, "Aw, what the hell . . ."

As I waited for my bus, across the street from TV Heaven, I watched with quiet amusement as the two of them pantomimed their impressions of our encounter to one another. After her argumentative manner was calmed by her supervisor, I saw Gail shake her head vigorously, as if rattling some demons loose before they could take hold. The manager patted her on the back, as if to say *Forget it.* After ten to twenty minutes the bus came and I took a secluded seat where I could openly examine my purchase.

I tore into the factory-fresh shrink-wrapping and held the skinned imported box to my nose, sucking its factory smells of inks and plastic deep into my olfactory senses, sniffing like a dog in rut for traces of origin, telltale stories. There were no confessions to be found in the smell of the tape—the truth had long since dried while awaiting sale and shipment—but, after so long a wait, I was not about to sour my evening with disappointments.

The particular excitement of buying an authorized edition of *Throat Sprockets* was the anticipation of a completely unblemished print—not those battered 35mm reels that made the rounds at indoor raincoat festivals, or the blurred, short-lived bootleg cassette I had acquired from the man with the goods, but a direct transfer from the film's original negative, with complete credits, without a single disruptive splice, with everything previously concealed restored and stripped bare, at last, for my eyes alone.

• • •

Who are you, Dark Lady, and why do you have this effect on me? Why is your particular aura something that only I can see? What instruction does your image communicate? What is it about your eyes that seems so brutally cold and barren, yet so inviting? I've heard that nomads survive the oppressive heat of the Sahara by swathing themselves in heavy garments, to keep the heat out; are your eyes, then, an extended promise of a cold even colder than the

*single life I've inherited, a cold that might enfold me and insulate me from my
winter of discontent? If your eyes are the windows to your soul, then to what is
your throat a window? Why do I admire to distraction the tautly stretched
canvas of your translucent skin? What is it about the flawed skin that veils
your veins, the veins that cage your muscles, the muscles that band about your
bones?*

*What is it that haunts me about your neck in a pose of flexion? Your neck
in a pose of rotation? Your throat in a pose of extension? What is the power of
its lateral aspect? The sight of your nape, its posterior aspect? The overwhelming allure of its anterior aspect? What is it in me that responds like a solemn
answer to the formidable questions you pose, and why can't I get at it? Will I
ever know?*

*Is the taste of your blood the only answer, the only cure for this fascina-
tion? This abyss that lies between us, between fact and fantasy, is it possible to
traverse it? Can I trapeze from this worn living-room chair to your bared
trapezius? Or will I fall somewhere between and lose everything? Or am I in
fact experiencing that fall, as you extend into forever, towering above and
beyond my reach?*

• • •

There was good news and there was bad news.

The Japanese import of *Throat Sprockets* looked absolutely
splendid; the image resolution was perfectly lifelike, but in terms
of content this authorized release was by far the least complete
print I had seen, lacking not only the massage and hotel sequences, but also the pivotal scene of the spilled wine. Also
against my expectations it was otherwise an *exact* reproduction of
the film as I had seen it at the Eros, at the House of Usherettes,
and on Hood's cassette. Every splice was identical, Pavlovian, as
strangely contributory to the film's spell and character as the
whorls of its maker's own fingerprint. That night I rewound the
tape knowing for the first time that what had been done to me
had been no accident.

It had been nothing less than a conscious and deliberate act of
terrorism.

• • •

I had proven myself at work to the extent that I was soon granted the executive privilege of setting the perimeters of my own eight-hour workday. That fall I started arriving at the office around noon, working until eight o'clock, and taking my lunch at four. This revamped timetable provided me with an additional five hours of darkness in the evening, ideal conditions for television viewing in my apartment; I spent this time watching *Throat Sprockets*, remembering the details of its missing scenes, and editing together on the flatbed of my imagination additional sequences that I pretended were filmed but not included in the final assembly.

With no theaters left downtown where I could take my lunch, I was forced to eat in restaurants like everyone else. Since Sarno's Italian Restaurant now had unpleasant associations for me, I ate there only when I found myself in a downbeat, reflexive mood; in other words, about as often as I had once cruised Widow's Peak. On other days, when my sense of ennui was dominant, I followed the course of least resistance and took the office elevator to the top floor of the Sutton Building, where there was an overpriced little penthouse bistro called Only the Best. My photograph must have been included in some directory of executives working in the building, because the maître d' greeted me by name on my very first visit.

In the weeks before her departure from SPI it was not uncommon for me to see Myla Monteith having an early supper there. She was always alone. She ordered Spartan meals and cleaned her plates with a grudging air of duty, as if the food gave her no pleasure. I, on the other hand, ordered my meals with a real sense of appetite, but ate very little; only a few bites, followed by coffee and cigarettes, which I would extinguish in uneaten, picture-perfect portions of steak tartar or veal florentine. With no companion to divert me with conversation I silently dwelled on the remembered details of her muscular black throat, its caramel highlights and dark chocolate shadings; these details had become more attractive, more intensive, since her collars had quietly risen some weeks before. Myla was certainly aware of my presence in the restaurant, but seemed strangely determined to avoid me, even though my assumption of the TV Heaven campaign should by rights have given us much to talk about. Perhaps she felt my eyes studying her, trying to analyze the reason behind her sudden escape into conservative fashions, through the smoke of my cigarettes. There were days when she deliberately seated herself with her back turned to me, and there were also days when she steeled herself to face me, her eyes downcast with most strenuous discipline as she picked at her nouvelle cuisine. I have never forgotten how those eyes once flashed up at me, brown and bottomless, as I rushed out of the solarium to pay for food I had been too nervous to eat.

I can now trace my sense of terror during those nonencounters to the absence of the restaurant scene from my import cassette of *Throat Sprockets*. The hotel sequence had been missing when I saw it at Chicago's House of Usherettes, and the more I thought about it, Nancy Reagan and I were drawn to one another by an overwhelming desire to make the film whole again, as we did by reenacting its missing scene that same night. The disappearance of the scene that preceded the introduction of the film's most haunting character could mean, I convinced myself, only one thing: *She was about to enter my life.*

Each afternoon as I crossed the orange carpet to my customary table, I was simultaneously frightened and piqued by the prospect of tipping over my wineglass, looking across the room, and locking into her returned gaze. Was it possible, I thrilled, that Myla Monteith would be revealed to me as the Dark Lady of the film I lived when *Throat Sprockets* slept in its box?

Negative.

After a week or so of stimulating discomfort Myla took her leave of absence from Sutton Perry & Ingersoll. There had been whispers of why and who, mostly among the other women in the office; I deliberately avoided listening. She did not share any words of farewell with me, but after seeing her off with the others I returned to my office to find her potted cactus installed on my desk. There was no card, nor did there really need to be.

It liked to show its spines, but it actually drank very little.

THE PROSCENIUM

THE ACCELERATION OF MY PROFESSIONAL LIFE WAS MYSTERIOUSLY INTER-
woven with an increasing fear of forward movement on all
other levels. Though Maverick Motors had generously offered to
consecrate our successful alliance with a Necromancer LTD, I was
content to continue riding the Metro to and from work, where
my Necromancer campaign—though almost a year old—was still
represented on the heralds above each window and the steering
was left to other hands. Some people viewed my preference to let
others do my driving for me as an irresponsibility on my part, a
reluctance to seize the reins of my own life. I disagreed; it was not
reluctance, but rather a fascination to see where the uncontested
tide of circumstance would take me. Nor could my orientation
reasonably be deemed irresponsible, for my reluctance to interact
with women during this stage of my life—another fear of progres-
sion—went against my natural inclinations and therefore was the
greatest possible proof of my responsibility. While my colleagues
assumed that my isolated life-style was a reaction to my divorce
("Once bitten," they liked to say), it was more truthfully based in
my memory of that ugly evening in Chicago where dreams and
films had been dared to come true. It seemed that whenever I

became interested in a woman, I became acutely aware of how she transmitted intimations of her secret self to knowing eyes with any number of signals, signals so outward and mundane that only I seemed aware of their currency as a secret language—not unlike the hidden messages I continued to discover with each new viewing of *Throat Sprockets*. Once I had observed how these messages were expressed by individual women, I came to recognize at a glance how they were expressed by all women; for example, while passively observing my fellow passengers on the Metro, I noticed that most of the women wore one or more rings of one sort or another. Much as an amethyst or emerald communicates a specific month of birth, the infinitely variable combinations of rings seemed to broadcast cryptographic messages, each configuration signaling a different resumé of the wearer. *I'm attached. I'm looking. I'm not looking. I'm married. I'm a widow. I'm brokenhearted. I'm unfaithful. I have a lover. I'm a lesbian. I'm a spendthrift. I'm trouble.* (If you see a woman wearing a ring on each of her fingers, *that's* trouble.) It was impossible to decipher the subtler variations. What, I wondered, was signified by a ring worn on the middle finger? By a ring worn on the third finger of the *right* hand? By a ring worn on a golden chain necklace? By the unseasonal wearing of gloves? Given a choice of subtexts to peruse, I pushed women away and ran down the sinewy aisle of my navel toward the images on the towering screens of theaters long since torn down.

I felt somewhat better equipped to deal with the conundrums posed by the secret tongues of turtleneck sweaters and scarves, which were finding renewed popularity in America for the first time since the sixties, our unanimous response to a fashion trend that news commentators had traced back to Stockholm and Tokyo. The interested observer might not glean immediate answers from a throat swathed in an ascot or turtleneck collar, but at least one was familiar with the questions posed by such investments. A woman with a covered throat either had good reason to conceal it or, at the very least, was sufficiently aware of the growing subcul-

ture to feel a shade of intimidation about leaving the house with
her throat exposed. Either explanation was enticing.

I was deep in the midst of some such rumination, when the
Metro's regular swing through Friendship Mall made the notion
of wandering through tides of oncoming faces and throats, before
succumbing to another solitary dinner, suddenly very attractive to
me. Scarcely before I realized I had made the decision, I found
myself inside the mall, breasting wave after wave of circulating
strangers as I passed a display of the latest fashions—modeled by
headless metal mannequins, all neck and fanned fingers—and
moved on toward the central atrium. Inside, the stores were
adorned with as many X's as the old Eros, *Xmas* being the key
word on exhibit. I found Xmas, too, being dismantled, sold off,
torn down. I can frame the moment of my visit in time only by
recalling that the postholiday sales were down to slim pickings,
and the Xmas decorations were in the process of being replaced
in storage. So who is to say if the year was at an end or just
beginning?

I took the escalator to the upper level. Unlike some other customers, who ran up the moving stairway to conserve precious
shopping time, I preferred to stand perfectly still—not advancing
to my destination, but rather submitting to the pull of my destiny.
Upstairs, other shoppers were going about their affairs: there was
a middle-aged man sitting on a bench, staring in space, waiting
for his wife to step out of Grab A Wave with new hair . . .
another was wearing spectacles with a bandaged bridge, loitering
outside the one-hour optical shop . . . some children were pulling on their foot-weary mothers, demanding comics and candy
. . . when I heard a ruckus on the other side of the atrium.

Curiosity guided me to the site of chaos. I saw a young mother
lift a child in her arms and hurry away, protecting its new shoes
from some obscene shape speeding toward them at ground level,
and then I took the step that brought the rest of the scene into
full view: a liquid red tongue was extending across the marbled

flooring outside an art supplies store called La Proscenium. The flow soon reached the limit of its outward movement, and I knelt at its outermost edge to examine it. Its hue was bloodred and movie-bright; its smell chemical, not biological. It exuded no cooling temperature, no fading warmth. The fantasy of the moment faltered.

It was *paint*.

My eyes as I knelt followed the spill back to its source and—there she stood.

Like a figure from my own subconscious she knelt at the opposite end of the pooling color—brunette and sullen-looking—in jeans and a pale green crew-neck sweatshirt. Our stances were identical. *Over the spill her deep purple eyes connect with his.* Every time I shifted position, or moved my head or my arms, I found that she copied my movements with almost studied precision; it seemed to be her obtuse method of acknowledging me. After a moment or two we simultaneously rose and moved instinctively toward each other, each of us able to bear the other's presence only by focusing instead upon the scarlet stream that formed a bonding bridge between us.

I took a few backward steps to let her pass. She took a few forward steps and hooked her dark, shoulder-length hair behind a lobeless ear; the adjustment permitted a lateral view of her throat, the hollow of its saltbox, the mild traces of perspiration in its young, tender, indefinite creasings, its strong slope into her crew-neck collar, its bold birthmark. I ransacked my mind for something to say and, unable to summon anything of my own worth using, fell back on a line of dialogue from *Throat Sprockets*:

"Veronica Lake, I presume?"

She offered no more than a flat, tacit hum of agreement; there was nothing in this sound that responded to the humor inherent in my observation, or suggested an awareness of its source, or indeed that ventured comment on anything other than the problem posed by the spill itself. Once she had walked entirely around the immense crimson comma, our eyes met again . . . but it was perhaps too soon for such conspiracies; the denied connection was too tenuous to hold with half insistence, and she turned her back to me, sauntering back into the store. I followed her inside, where she ignored me as she would her own shadow.

Inside La Proscenium the ambient Muzak that flowed throughout the mall rose to a more noticeable register. "Hey, Viv?" she called, addressing the wall at the rear of the store. "We've got a little problem out here."

Her voice was reedy and tinged with a casual dry accent, which triggered my inward smile as I drifted toward a cluttered aisle of color markers, index cards, and binders. Did she mean me? *Too fast, too fast.*

The voice of her co-worker winced from the rear office. "What now?"

"Some paint got tipped over."

"How much?"

"A gallon pail."

There was a groan. "What color?"

"Nothing too ostentatious . . . vermilion red." As she filed her report, she slumped glumly over the front counter, her body language overacting as if to reach the back rows of the theater—or at least to the aisle of color markers, index cards, and binders.

The woman called Viv cursed with equal color and, as she emerged from the back rooms, turned white with embarrassment at my unexpected presence. "Excuse me," she apologized, casting a cold, reproachful glance at the other.

"Oh, yeah, we have a customer," mentioned the moody employee. She said the word *customer* as if she were pointing out a Democrat to a roomful of Republicans.

In the following days and weeks I continued to drop by La Proscenium for items I didn't need, little things that the agency could have easily provided. I would stand at the counter, patiently holding my index cards or gum erasers or filing labels, exhilarated by her sulky manner as she dealt with other customers and their observations about the weather and questions of measurement. The angle at which she stood while totaling my purchases, without offering the slightest assent of our under-the-counter communication, provided me with an ideal view of the mole on her throat, which rode her pulse like a public nipple. In idle moments I found myself wondering where this genetic heirloom had appeared on her mother, her grandmother, and even more distant relatives—how much trouble and happiness they had derived from it in the forgotten moments of their own lives—as if I wanted to ravish not only her but her entire bloodline. I always paid by check to leave her in possession of my name and address. This was more than she had given me to encourage my own wildly outspiraling dream, and as I watched my Japanese cassette of *Throat Sprockets* in the evenings, its content was made more intense, more immediate, by the constant possibility that she might interrupt it at any given point by loitering in the hall outside my apartment or, on a brazen impulse, actually lean on my doorbell. As the days wore into weeks, I became familiar with the cars that were always present in the parking area allotted to her shop, and wondered which of these vehicles might be hers. Among them was a red Necromancer. Had my campaign reached her as well? I wondered if this might be the root of our connection. . . .

Throughout this twilight period I had two dreams—one waking, one sleeping. Waking, I imagined what might happen if I found myself stranded some evening at the mall with no means of getting home. I imagined myself turning to her, and pictured myself as a passenger in her Necromancer, racing upstream by her side through cometing headlights, arriving at a darkened underpass and taking the wheel and her throat at the same moment. . . . But sleeping—that was when the *truth* came out. In my dreams she was never anything but the dark-eyed stranger she was in factual daylight. There were the dour and dolorous dreams in which she passed me by, oblivious of the muffled sound of my breaking heart, and then there were the more common tortures in which I felt her presence near, my awareness touched by her palpable presence behind the door of some adjoining room I couldn't enter.

I didn't know how to approach her, or what I wanted from her.

One question kept coming back to me: *Could this be love?* I had married Paige in our late teens . . . *could this be how love felt in my thirties?* But isn't love supposed to make us happy? Doesn't love make us want to take the object of our affections out into the wide open spaces, to commune with and celebrate existence, to share experiences, create bonds, find ourselves? How then could I explain that my most urgent desire where this woman was concerned was to jump past all those things, beyond the trivia of our favorite colors and formative encounters with love and sex and death, and take her in my arms and shut us both away somewhere small and dark and tight, where loud, sad music could pommel us, overwhelm and propel us beyond judgment, beyond all human laws and accountability?

I didn't know how to approach her, or what I wanted from her. I would take the Metro home from La Proscenium, having seen her, seared and discouraged by yet another failure to move forward on my part, and spend the evening watching *Throat Sprockets,* inhabiting *Throat Sprockets.* I was beyond ordinary viewings by this time, and would fast-forward through scenes, slow them down to make new connections, to smell the roses, to ignore the memorized main action in favor of the revelatory blur and minutiae. Or I would alter my consciousness with certain amenities, which lubricated my thought processes and prodded still other connections to the surface. No matter how much I tried to distract myself—by addressing the film academically, microscopically, synthetically—I could not escape the fact that the appearance of this strange woman in the play of my life made the film seem less mysterious and altogether less fantastic. I left the blinds on my living-room windows down for days, watching and drinking, watching and smoking, watching as the nameless actress—whom this girl in my life resembled—succumbed again and again to the invasive seductions of the Glover, muttering to myself in a drone of depression that I would never be clean again. I thought of her ceaselessly, and just as often, with equal passion and dread, I considered buying a gun. I didn't know how to approach her, or what I wanted from her.

Jesus, I thought. *Love sucks.*

I didn't know how to approach her, but I felt so astonishingly alive in the uncertainties of the meantime . . . wandering through the aisles at La Proscenium, pausing at the side of their complimentary coffee machine and its stacked pagoda of foam cups, wondering if she would ever change the green sweatshirt she wore each day, or if we were caught forever in an obsessively repeated memory of our first meeting, pretending to appraise the T-squares, the blotters and binders, all motionless, all camouflage around my accelerating heart. And then, one day when the store was all but empty, out of nowhere two arms enveloped me from behind, and I heard her say:

"What can I do . . . to *stop* this?"

"The only way to stop this," I told her, "is to *start* it."

She planted her lips between my shoulder blades. "I thought you'd never ask."

• • •

A stranger cuts through your life as a kindred shadow, a shape that somehow fits between the outline of the child you imagine having and the mate you aspire to be. You risk rejection, and once across that ragged bridge, you must build for that other person in words a representation of the unquestioned person you have only previously been within the walls of your self; in essence, you *cram* —years into moments, complexities into clichés, reducing a storm of desire into calm cordiality.

Her name was Emma Mitsouko, but it in no way resembled her.

I had come to regard her as X, which was so expressive of her simplicity and cool, forbidding quality. To understand the true authority of an X, don't put it in front of a movie theater—put it in front of a woman.

"I didn't know how to approach you," I told her over a candle at Sarno's, "or what I wanted from you."

We exchanged our lives in nutshells. I explained that I had always lived in Friendship, that I had gone through small agonies as each of my friends had moved away to seek higher adventure; that a former marriage and a good job had more or less stranded me there. This prompted from her an intersecting explanation of how she had been the oldest of two children, how her brother had committed suicide in his early teens, and how she had escaped this and other squalid memories of her Nova Scotia hometown by majoring in film studies at Ohio State University, where she had dropped out after a couple of semesters due to diminished funds; she questioned me. I explained that I worked in advertising, that some of my ideas had been filmed as commercials in Hollywood, that I had been barred from the sets on more than one occasion by insecure directors; I questioned her. She explained that the La Proscenium thing was only temporary, a favor to her friend Viv, whose regular associate was not well; that she made a modest but happy living in ceramics, consigning her wares to various shops around the city. After a leery pass at each, we found ourselves similarly disinclined to discuss sports, our families, politics, or our former relationships. The subject of my marriage was safe ground only when mentioned as a historical point of reference.

"Your marriage is over and friends are gone, so it's just your job that's keeping you here?"

"At this point I could find work anywhere," I told her. "But since the divorce I seem to have a problem with moving forward."

She smirked. "I've noticed."

We continued to talk, to joke, to speechify, to calm one another's fears, to confide and confess. Even as we laughed, I felt
conscious of an almost symphonic tragedy circling around and
around our dinner table. You know the feeling: *Now that I've found
you, what will I do if I lose you?* Then, out of the blue, I expressed a
curiosity that I felt quite genuinely but couldn't rationally explain.

"I wonder," I said, "if I were to tell you a little white lie—not
that I have, you understand—but if I did, I wonder if you would
pick up on that? I wonder if it would prompt another one from
you?"

Emma's pupils dilated with inviting dark. "I just told one," she
smiled, "and you've just responded to it."

She apologized for having been untrue by touching my hand,
the kind of touch that comes from a rescuing grip that lets you
go, then saves you again, taunting your security to lend trust
renewed meaning. We were strangers to one another, she and I,
but somehow familiar beneath ourselves, implicated with one
other in abhorrent mystery.

We took our conversation to her loft. Like her redundant but
practical tastes in clothing, Emma's furniture seemed to have
nothing to do with the woman she was; the pieces were mostly
secondhand acquisitions that didn't quite match one another,
chosen primarily for utility, practicality, and comfort. This was
someone with little time or regard for appearances, who preferred
to concentrate on the furnishings of her interior life. Her apartment had the appeal of a museum in miniature. Each of her
rooms, including the kitchen area, was lined with musty used
hardcovers (no paperbacks) devoted to Japanese and Indian culture, mythology, cooking, anatomy; the arcane sobriety of the
place was punctuated here and there with amusing little accents
like trout-shaped oven mitts and peculiar newspaper clippings
that she fixed to the door of her refrigerator with bar magnets. I
read one as Emma powdered her nose:

BOOMER, West Virginia—Mildred Hapmeier, 43, was admitted to Montgomery General Hospital late Tuesday, after being struck by lightning in Windsor Park's trailer camp, according to local authorities. The victim was struck at approximately 8:15 P.M. while passing under an elm tree near a shortcut trail through the parkgrounds. The accident site was approximately two blocks from her home. Ms. Hapmeier reportedly slept for forty-eight hours and awoke complaining of thirst. It is a common symptom of lightning victims to experience extreme, unquenchable thirst.

We talked in her living room area as the hours grew smaller and smaller, answers bouncing back from questions—indeed, questions bouncing back from questions—as if there was nothing between us but a porous, pliable mirror.

"Why the interest in Japanese and Indian culture?"

"It's in my blood, actually, a little of both," she explained.

I could see it in her face as soon as she mentioned it. She could tell that I was only now noticing, and this tickled her. "It's the first thing everyone else notices." She laughed.

"Japanese culture has always struck me as being very ethereal," I said later, while examining some of the artifacts she had collected, "but Indian culture is somehow the opposite. They're complementary mysticisms, aren't they? Like earth and air?"

Emma removed a bottle, two thirds full, of Bell's whisky from an antique cabinet. "Firewater?" she proposed.

She dispensed the amenity in equal portions, then led me to the opposite end of the loft, where she worked. She had allotted more room to her art than to her life, which said a great deal about her. Her studio was a spacious domain, walled with brickwork, with a single barred window dominated by a godawfully bright streetlamp on the other side; her glazed ceramic vases, unfinished statuary, a framed sheet of glass made blindingly white by the outside streetlamp, and miscellaneous pieces in terra-cotta stood in orbits around the nuclei of her kiln and potter's wheel.

"Show me what you do here," I urged.

Emma drained her glass in one gulp and settled into the seat above the pedal wheel as if it were the humming saddle of a Harley-Davidson, looking eased and strengthened. She removed her rings and placed them ceremoniously on a nearby dish towel. Now ready, she unwrapped a brick of fresh clay from a nearby stack—staring at me throughout its undraping as if executing a stylish striptease—and hurled it, *thwack*, onto the wheel. Spritzing it with a plant mister, she began pedaling it in circles, mothering its mass with knowing hands.

"Earth and water." I grinned.

I lit a Consolations, determined to bond the smell of my cigarettes with this moment so that I might replay it again and again at future convenience. I exhaled.

"Fire and air," she rejoined.

I gave her a draw on my cigarette and began to drift around her studio, leaving her to concentrate on her clay, which zoomed tall in response to her manipulations. Her work was intriguing, her vases without exception tall and slender, vaguely organic looking, and stippled with texture. I admired her sense of vision and craftsmanship, and I felt myself becoming intoxicated by the repetitious, almost mantralike rhythm of her wheel's rotation and the sight of her dusty ankle boot pressing, pressing, to keep that rhythm alive and steady.

"These are very good," I said, commenting on some pieces near the window. (They really were.)

She looked over her shoulder at me. "Oh, you can't really appreciate the detail with all that light, can you? Pull that shade down. Don't worry, it's loosely woven; the room will still have light. The shine off this poster frame over here is giving me a headache, anyway."

I slowly lowered the shade, happy to be useful. As she had predicted, the shade helped to diminish the blinding glare on a large poster frame in front of her, the contents of which were revealed as the screen descended; I lowered the blind all the way to the sill. I walked to the wall where the poster hung in awed silence. Before me once again was the one-sheet poster for *Throat Sprockets,* its folds steamed flat but otherwise exactly as I had seen it that first afternoon at the Eros, almost two years before. My reaction to the poster was more than mere admiration; it was transfixion, conveyance, a temporary but nonetheless complete and blissful loss of self.

"Where did you ever find it?"

"There was a sale at the old Eros Theater downtown. It was only three dollars."

"You were there?"

"Why not? I'm over eighteen."

"I was there too. At the sale. I looked all over for this, but it was gone."

"I found it first."

"So I see."

"If you were so desperate to find it," she continued, "then you must know something about it." It was an intuitive statement, but she made it sound like a pointed question or accusation. Perhaps the words sounded more emphatic because of the sudden silence in the room; her wheel had fallen still.

"I don't know anything about it."

"Nothing?" She persisted.

"Less and less, in fact."

"I know what you mean," she said.

"Have you ever seen—" I wasn't able to complete the thought, as it was obliterated by the shape formed by her hands on the potter's wheel. Perhaps it was another shape left unfinished in the drama of our dialogue, but as it was, it was a rough but perfect rendering of a human throat, slender and athletic, impeccable, catholic, androgynous. And then I saw the detail I hadn't seen before—that all of the vases I had been admiring were assorted likenesses of napes and necks. "But of course you have," I finished.

Emma's complexion was now flushed with anxiety and arousal, as she regarded me with hard eyes. I knew what was behind that hardness in her eyes; she was sorting through her feelings about me. I was preoccupied with similar calculations, adding up our agreements, our disagreements, and the consequences of those hard eyes. Once your sums are checked, there is nothing left to discuss.

Either you do, or you don't.

If you do, it's done desperately the first time, with prefatory apologies for how quick it's bound to be, and followed by a complete, withdrawn silence—the smoker's pardon. It's the time to expulse, not yet to express. You may go at one another for days without saying a word to one another during the act, or you may fall back on the scenarios and dialogue of the cinema, playacting to keep the gravity of what is happening from seeming as gravid as it is. In time comes trust and the true language, the preverbal sounds we reserve for the ears of significant others. That language is forged between two people into a key to the red rooms where we keep our screams and our childhoods and orgasms in disarray on a torn linoleum floor, where every tear we've ever shed is shelved in cracked, chronological jars; that key opens the locks on chambers so loud with pain and pleasure that the clatter of the rattles in our cribs can't be told from the rattle of the handcuffs in our hells . . . where the walls are so red with fire and flushedness that you barely notice the burst of color when . . .

It would be wrong to say more than this, because it was *ours*, what happened between us, that first time. As the narration in *Throat Sprockets* says, in the celebrated moment when the screen goes black for twenty-five seconds:

The blank pages of life
    are most blessed,
when the chaos of desire weds
    the pulse of allure,
and a taste of intent.
They cloud over like ouzo,
when stirred or disturbed,
and the two float as one
nameless, placeless energy
with the Gestating,
the Dreaming, and the Dead.

Dawn. Cigarettes. Emma broke through the faint music of morning birdsong with my name. "How many times have you seen it?" she asked.

"It's far beyond numbers, I'm afraid."

"I see."

"How about you?"

"Once."

"Only once?"

She nodded her head, affirmatively.

"Where was that, at the Eros?"

"No," she said, slightly irritably. "I'd have never gone into that place while it was open."

"Where, then?"

"You won't believe this, but I really can't remember."

"I can believe that. There's a lot of things I can't remember. The real things, mostly."

She pinched my chest and smiled. "Remember me?"

"When the brain forgets, the soul still remembers. That's how strangers meet and come together."

"You're a reincarnationist?"

"No," I said, "but the third king of Persia was."

She got the joke, and it seemed to energize her. "So," she said, coming closer to my face, "are you up for another go?"

"Another go at you, or the tape?"

Helplessly, reflexively, her fingers gripped—almost gouged—me, as if I were one of her clay things. She almost wailed.

"You have it *on tape*!?"

• • •

I awoke on the rug at the foot of our bed, with a blanket draped thoughtfully over me. I was used to waking to wafting breakfast smells and the gurgling sounds of our Mr. Coffee, or to the noise of the construction team ripping up the imperfect road at the end of our street. As consciousness became more definite, I focused on the objects in the room—a portable television, a wicker hamper, small Indian vases, an open closet stuffed with more books than clothing (green sweatshirts and jeans), a throw rug between the bed and the door, and, most impressively, an Oriental partition of indeterminate age bearing a watercolored triptych of winged spirits at war—and realized that I had seen none of these things before; in fact, I remembered only the most selective information beyond what I'd gleaned from the confirmation of Emma's almond-shaped eyes, only enough information to specifically plant my next step, my next kiss, my mouth on her throat.

I dressed in the breeze of an open window, sounds of passing cars and lawn mowers filtering through the screen, feeling such a spring in my step that even my necktie felt a welcome addition to the day. As I wriggled the knot upward in closure, the memory of a compliment from the night before swam to the surface: "I like your hands . . . and your mouth," she had said, "and I also like your . . ."

She had gestured toward what she meant, unable to find the appropriate word.

"What, my Adam's apple?"

"I hate that expression," she had complained. "Too biblical—besides, didn't the apple belong to Eve?"

"But she offered a bite to Adam. And it stuck."

"Too biblical," she said again.

"Larynx, then?"

"Such a fractious word for such a sexy thing. *Larynx* doesn't feel good in my mouth, when I say it."

"Then you'll have to invent a new one," I suggested. "I wonder what it's called in other languages?"

"In French it's spelled the same but pronounced differently— almost like the name Lawrence."

"*Lawrence* won't do. I won't have you calling any part of me by another man's name."

"In Spanish the word is *laringe*—a nice, soft word. Like *lozenge*."

"I guess *lozenge* might do. Care for an after-dinner lozenge?"

Reflecting on that episode I undid my tie, wound it into a coil, and stuffed my jacket's inner pocket with it, then unfastened the top button of my shirt. Another cardinal rule of the art of advertising: Give the people what they want.

I found Emma in the kitchen area, dressed again in the clothes she wore like a recurring dream, holding an empty coffee mug on the crook of one finger, her other hand resting on the subtle curve of her hip.

"I thought I heard you up and around," she said, pouring a second cup for me. "You like it black, don't you . . . when you can't have it red?"

The comment would have been offensive coming from anyone else. Her coffee was delicious, a connoisseur's blend with a distinctly berry bouquet. She placed her cup beside the sink and pulled me gently to her, grasping the back of my neck and pressing my mouth, still warm with coffee, to her throat. Under my closed eyes she gave a deep groan, the sound people reserve for neck rubs, for hot showers, for the taste of that first margarita on summer vacation. She told me that my warm lips felt good, then asked me to have some more coffee.

". . . but don't swallow."

Curiously, I complied with her request, taking a small amount of coffee into my mouth. Emma took a small step backward, shaking back the curtain of her shoulder-length hair in a gesture some women use to appear attractive or dashing or otherwise preoccupied to a stranger . . . revealing a medium-sized, dot-shaped bandage where her mole had been. Gingerly she peeled the bandage away from a small bruise in which, on closer inspection, I saw an impression of my own front teeth.

"It's a little sore this morning," she explained. "Just put your mouth *right on it*, okay?"

I did as she asked, allowing no coffee to spill from my lips, holding its soothing warmth against her sprockets. She chuckled at my readiness.

"I didn't think I'd have to tell you twice. No biting, now. Oh! That feels *soooooooo good.*"

Holding my mouth against that place on her throat that ticked like a tiny clock, I suppressed the desire to ask her how last night had been; I felt a niggling suspicion that absolutely no reference should be made to the increasing number of scenes that were missing lately from my own life. *Variety is the splice of life,* I thought.

In time she smoothed the back of my head, softly but sternly, a signal to break contact that came back to me like a splash of cold water from the night before. I swallowed my mouthful of coffee, Brand X, and watched her with interest as she redressed her wound. She did it as nicely as Paige used to remove her brassiere.

"I hope I'm halfway presentable," I said, suppressing a mild shudder, remembering the reflection I had once cast into the mirror of a certain hotel room. "Where's the bathroom?"

Emma apologized and gave me the necessary directions. Then she added, "I'm surprised you don't remember. When you're ready, we'll take our party to your place."

"No La Proscenium today?"

"No La Proscenium today. Just you and me and our—friend from Japan."

"Sounds good to me."

Passing through the bathroom door required some effort. Through a broad slash in my spirit, dread was slowly siphoning away the youth I had felt upon awakening. Marshaling my courage I looked into the mirror of her medicine chest and felt an almost seasonal calm take possession of me. My reflection was as young as my feelings of renewal had indicated, my skin of yellowing guilts now a thing of the past. I rinsed my mouth, and spat pinkish water into the sink. I stole a peek inside her medicine cabinet, reading the ringlike insinuations of her ibuprofen and estrogen tablets, her lubricants, creams, and coagulants, and the package labeled Cross. Feeling ripe for a shower I slid open its opaque pebbled glass door and found the shower's porcelain floor smattered with small russet stains. . . .

I was bombarded with flashes—like frames of deleted footage —of joy and agony, advantage and expenditure. I had opened two doors, but was able to close only one.

• • •

Emma drove us to my place. It occurred to me, while she was visiting my bathroom, that I had never watched *Throat Sprockets* on video with another person in the room; it wouldn't be as conveniently anonymous as seeing it in a vast and darkened auditorium among strangers. Would I feel as free, in her company, to touch myself, or would she sense my particular needs at any given moment and service them for me? I experienced a surge of discomfort—not unlike a threat of exposure—as she wafted back and ("May I?") fed my import cassette into the VCR. In the dimmed room ("That's better") her breathing sounded as irregular as mine, and as she placed a liter bottle of Evian between us on the module sofa ("Just in case"), she murmured with audible stress, "I can tell, this is going to be real, real *bad*. . . ."

I pressed the Play button of my remote, and she raised her legs onto the couch, burying the lower half of her face behind her knees.

Immediately, I pressed Pause. "Look," I said, "let's not . . . let's *try* not to get lost in this, okay?"

"How do you mean?"

"I don't know. Maybe we should try watching it, just this once, with the sound off."

She tacitly agreed to this, then asked if we should put on some music of our own to compensate.

I had another plan. "Why don't we discuss the film as we watch it? Comment, annotate, free-associate, if that's what we feel like doing. I'll tell you what I see, you tell me what you see. We're bound to have noticed different things, don't you think?"

"So you'll do what, give me the Male Perspective?"

"I guess so, and you can give me yours. And we can tell each other what we're really seeing, and not just what we're imposing on the film out of our own personal delusions."

"Sounds okay with me," she said, leaning back against the sofa. "What if we get turned on?"

"Let's cross that bridge when we come to it."

Pause released, *Throat Sprockets* began.

I drew her attention to the splice that occurred after the fade-out of "Lotus Films Presents," pointing out that the splice was made at the very instant a throat first appeared onscreen; hence, this could be read as a "cut throat." I also observed a repetition of the "cut throat" motif as the stems of a dozen red roses were scissored and dropped down the neck of a slender vase. Lingering shot of the submerged thorns beading with bubbles.

"The print has turned red," I noted. "The color fading would date this film somewhere in the nineteen sixties, wouldn't it?"

"The color hasn't faded at all," she countered. "The images have been *tinted* red, which is a completely different matter. See? The colors are still quite strong under that rose-colored filter. This film could have been made yesterday."

After several extended sequences photographed on indoor sets Emma surprised me once again by pointing out a location shot that I had never noticed. The camera was attentively trained on a full-frame detail of the bare tanned throat of a brunette in her thirties, her shoulder-length hair blowing across it in dark wisps like lacerations. I thought I saw a small mole riding her pulse, but before I could confirm this, the actress stepped out of frame to reveal—behind her—a split-second view of a fabulous construction as futuristic as it was medieval.

We rewound and reviewed the disclosure several times. Emma identified the structure as the Sagrada Familia Cathedral in Barcelona. "It was begun as an experiment in improvisational architecture in the late eighteen hundreds," she explained. "The architect was a man named Gaudí. He was run over by a car in the nineteen twenties, but the work continued. Even today it's far from finished."

"Have you been there?" I asked.

"Sure," she claimed. "I've even been inside."

I suggested that the cathedral looked laryngeal. *"Laringe,"* she muttered, settling deeper into the flow of images.

We fell under the film's spell even *mit out sound* (the way it had been shot, after all) and said no more until a woman's lips read aloud from a menu in tight close-up. I punned, "The menu is red." I also observed that her mouth was like a wound.

"No," Emma insisted. "Her mouth is *against* a wound; it's a double exposure, a subliminal or something."

I accused her of making that up. At her insistence we replayed the scene in slow motion. Not only was the woman's mouth over-printed with a single subliminal frame of the Dark Lady's throat sprockets, borrowed from the climax of the film, but a restaurant patron in the background of the shot was raising a glass of wine to his lips in the same frame. My charming X had marked the spot.

I suggested that the entire restaurant scene had been constructed to leave the brunette at its center feeling vulnerable. I enumerated her broken high heel, her mispronunciation of the dishes on the menu, the intervention of the man fidgeting with the knot of his necktie. My watchful companion responded by suggesting that the fidgeting wasn't a real tic at all, but rather a technique intended to hypnotize this young woman.

"Wait!" she shouted. "There's another one! Did you see that?"

"What?"

"Go back, go back. . . . *There!*"

Emma's acute vision had discerned the outline of Tivoli Gardens in the background of an especially misty shot. "In the course of a single stroll she has somehow managed to walk from Barcelona to Copenhagen."

"A continuity error."

"Not necessarily. It could be that she's so ripe for it, she doesn't know where she is anymore."

"Is that how it is—for you?" I wondered. "When you're feeling 'ripe,' as you say . . . do you feel like you don't know where you are anymore? Placeless?"

She made a hazy hum against me that could have meant anything, or nothing.

A good deal of time, particularly during the extended scene in the psychiatrist's office, passed in our mutual silence. We were being pulled into it. The film, with all its drinking and lip-licking and lip-locking, was a parching experience. Emma reached for the Evian water, drank some, then passed it to me. Of course, the tip of the bottle was wet. . . .

"This guy really has a thing for women's throats," I announced, taking my swig.

"Look who's talking," my companion chided. Then, after a long pause in which neither of us had fresh observations to offer, she asked: "What question keeps coming back to you, as you watch this?"

"Probably *Who is the artist?*" I told her. "No," I immediately corrected myself, "*Who did this to me?* That's the question that keeps coming back. *Who did this to me?* What about you?"

"I ask myself, *Who is the artist who did this to me?*"

"Any ideas? Any suspicions?"

She shook her head. "What about you? Do you know much about films?"

"Enough to hate what passes for films these days. This ain't John Ford, I'll tell you that much."

"For a long time I thought it might be Kurosawa. Despite the European locations the fetishism of this film is very Japanese, plus you have the book of Shakespeare. Kurosawa is known for his interpretations of Shakespeare. But . . ."

"But what?"

"But Kurosawa has a thing about rain. This movie is too fucking dry for Kurosawa." Emma took another pull on the Evian bottle and sank back into the film in a state of utter absorption, as good as alone in the room. "Let's be quiet now," she suggested, half absently.

"Are you proposing that I give my mouth a rest?"

"Rest it on me, if you like," she invited.

Surely you, too, recognize the dialogue from the film? Yes, without intending to, the two of us gradually found ourselves inhabiting the roles of the ciphers onscreen, guiding them through their adventures and speaking their lines like a couple of decadent gods couched atop Olympus, guiding opposing pawns to the predetermined downfall of an ancient game. Unconsciously my Dark Lady went through the motions of unfastening the invisible catch of a nonexistent collar. The Glover leaned over her, and leaning into her, I could smell the detergent freshness of her sweatshirt and a splash of fruity perfume that navigated a chemical shortcut from my nose to my sex. The Glover and I were as one, Emma X and the XXX actress—virtual lookalikes, the same "type"—were as one: our mouth fell to their soft and vulnerable skin, our teeth flattening against their throat, and we felt their pulse against our fillings. We chilled them; the lighting and microphotography captured the magical coarsening of their skin, thickening like an areola around an erect vein. Then we pulled our mouth away—but our lips, refusing to let go, held on. We sucked a soft flap of tissue between our eyeteeth, pinched it ever so delicately until their minute healings reopened. They quivered ever so slightly as we bit down, billowing gently from a broken backstage window. . . . .

The music of our unions was overwhelming, otherwise the Glover might have spoken in a voice-over with great emotion, about the delicacy of probing the jugular notch of a lover's throat, of finding the area that is most ticklish or resistant to exploration, for this sensation signifies the throat's erogenous zone. The area must be broken in, the annoyance it feels refined until it is redefined as a source of pleasure. He might have described the flavor of her yield and how it inspired in his drunken senses distinct but mysteriously braided emotions of longing and oblivion. Unlike sexual intercourse, he would say, the moment of entry marks the point of something like orgasm—*oralgasm?*—which pivots (at least for the male) on the flash of a highly personal, subjective image, not the specialized mental snapshots that guide lovers to genital climax, but images from the private touchstones of life that one associates with enigma or regret. It follows, quite naturally, that while one derives a feeling of requital from the act, there is no true lasting satisfaction. It needs to be done again. An afterglow of awareness spread through the four of us, of the moment that would come all too soon, when our partners would begin to feel faint at the extent of their giving and fear the immensity of our need, and caress our faces to make us stop, pushing us gently but firmly away, just as we found a connection to the one source where all is possible and nothing exists.

As our conjoined flesh once again withdrew into inconsolable opposites—mine from his, hers from hers, ours from each other's—the only truth we understood was that the wait for the next time had already begun.

MORE MERCHANDISE

EMMA AND I MANAGED TO FORGE OUR OWN PRIVATE WORLD IN A VERY short time, completely immersed in the film and ourselves, but the outside world soon knocked at our closed door with pressing demands of its own. Our first overnight separation came with the delivery date of my next campaign proposal, which I was required to present to the company's board of directors in Washington, D.C.

That campaign fell into my lap like all the others. I was at the office, smoking and reflecting on the many clever ways in which Emma and I had found to intersect and interact with *Throat Sprockets*, wondering where it would all lead, when the Old Man surprised me by slipping the half-spent cigarette from my fingers. It was the same brand I had smoked since that distant night in Chicago. With keen anthropological fascination Austin peered at the tiny red letters that lined the white shaft below the filter—CONSOLATIONS—his eyes brimming with mysticism.

"You *smoke* these," he said, half question, half instruction. His voice hoarded a kind of optimism.

I nodded. At this assent his snowy brows shot up, never to come down.

"We—meaning *you*, my young friend—just may have a crack at the Consolations account," he announced, buffing his fingernails on his breast pocket.

Before I could catch enough breath or humor to react, he removed a pack of Consolations tucked inside my shirt pocket. He took out a fresh cigarette and placed it between my lips, his manner intent and procedural as he fired its tip with his Statue of Liberty lighter. I suppressed my amusement by looking into his eyes, bright divining beads which communicated that he was at least half serious in this erratic performance, acting as the low priest in an age-old ritual, prefacing creative ignition with its own pantomime. I inhaled, my lungs swelling with heavy smoke and ethereal images. The pale blue orbs of his eyes seemed to spin as he watched me blow the smoke at an angle past his face.

"Look at this kid," he marveled. "He's already working on it."

•   •   •

On the afternoon before I left for Washington, I went to Emma's loft. Our previous encounter had been a bit too enthusiastic, leaving her too sore to indulge me, so we spent our time together in bed aimlessly conversing.

"Where do you think veins begin?" I asked her, my finger tracing the subtle blue line that glided from the edge of her lip, like drool, and down the lateral aspect of her throat.

"I don't understand."

"I'd like to find your first vein. Your source."

Emma hastened to the dominant position. "But there isn't an entrance—a 'source'—per se," she said, using the horns of my pelvis as her lectern. "The circulatory system is a sealed unity, like a cage."

I outlined her small breasts with my finger, stopping it near the center of her sternum. "Perhaps the entrance is somewhere inside the heart?"

"I don't think so. The only way into the heart is through the veins. Or through the chest cavity itself."

"I suppose you're right," I concluded, observing the mystery of her cage as it expressed itself in blue tracings under the skin of her neck, her temple, the joinings of her inquisitive fingers.

"Wait a minute," she said, sitting bolt upright on me. "I know where it is! I know where the first vein is!"

"Okay, where?"

She poked me dead center.

"It's your belly button." She laughed. "We're fed through the navel by the placenta as we grow in the womb. So the belly button is the route our first nourishment takes into our blood-stream. It's the mouth that breath takes away from us. It's the mouth we forget how to use."

"Thank God." I groaned. "If not, we'd be walking around like those party boys on *America's Funniest Home Videos*, with eyes painted on their nipples, whistling with their fat stomachs!"

"No," she insisted, climbing off, calming my objections. "Don't you remember? How wonderful it was? The way it closed you to everything? The way it closed you off from everything but the nourishment you took? The precious oblivion?"

I kissed her deeply, then I poked hers. "If we somehow managed to reactivate *yours*, would it kiss me?"

"Certainly not! A belly button doesn't give; it *takes*."

"That's all?"

"That's all. That's the uncomplicated beauty of it."

"Mine too?"

"Of course, yours too."

I climbed onto all fours, hovering like an animal above her abdominal pucker, crumpled like the lips of a balloon that's lost all color and elasticity, and whispered: "Let's wake it up."

She bit her lip: abyss.

I spat magic into her bull's-eye. Then I encircled her navel repeatedly with my tongue, its surface moisture seeming to penetrate deeper and deeper into her belly with each short revolution. She made the noises I knew she was capable of, as if each revolution was winding something inside her tighter and tighter, but I could feel nothing but an insulting nostalgia for a time of life when this kind of play had been enough to satisfy me. There was pleasure in it, but no release, no satisfaction; the greedy thirst of the navel is too legendary to quench, too old to awaken. There is no going back, for it ceases to exist once its liquid credo has passed into our bodies. That old taste of blood is forever denied us, bombed behind a debris of years, reachable only through simulations that are as peculiar as we can make them, as peculiar as we have ourselves been made. With these thoughts circling through my mind I realized that Emma and I were daring to go beyond, to reinvent what was already the reinvention of our secret selves.

Instinctively, feeling a terror I could not yet identify as presentiment, I pounced on her and sank my teeth into her sore spot, my mouth pressed tightly to the partner I was perhaps already beginning to lose.

Afterward, as I sat deep in thought on the edge of the mattress, Emma returned from the bathroom and, the way she described it, saw a pair of wings on her Oriental partition matched perfectly—from her perspective—to my shoulder blades.

Imagine what I felt when she called me "Angel Face."

•   •   •

I had been too irresponsibly preoccupied to prepare anything, and spent the hour-long flight to Washington desperately combing my consciousness for presentable ideas, unable to step—in any way but physically—outside the cul-de-sac of Emma's neck and shoulder. As more distance fell between us, the 747 raising me closer and closer to the thundering bosom of heaven, my thoughts were entirely possessed with broken, obsessive recordings of an attraction so advanced that it was no longer carnal, encompassing all the visceral sweetness of lust, betrayal, and tragedy with every heartbeat, a lovesickness that persisted even when reciprocated.

The buzz at Dulles Airport that evening was that the Cure were in town, and I watched with fascination as this troupe of fern-haired, powder-faced specters trudged with their entourage through the crowd toward a private exit. I had been familiar with the group since the early eighties, and knew them as specialists in electrically dense, oceanic self-pity. To my surprise the band were playing that night not to an intimate gathering of brooding young cognoscenti, as they had in my college days, but rather to a full house at RFK Stadium. Yesterday's bittersweet sorrow had somehow become the rallying cry of the mainstream. From the well-flattened backseat of my Bell taxi, I watched as car after car cut through the slushy streets, driven by painted porcupines en route to the stadium.

A discarded copy of *Billboard* lay crumpled on the floor, and I was prompted by the whorl of phenomena to study the week's Top 100. I was not quite expecting to find the trend sulking back at me from that weekly graph. Nearly all of the nation's hit songs, I noticed, had been recorded by mannish women and ambivalent men, with mournful lyrics tenderly addressed to the genderless lovers no longer in their lives. I recognized the symptom. All of us—the people who shaped society—were somehow touched by the same depression, and our blue funk was profiting no one but the businesses we represented in order to stay alive and in this pathetic state. To the record companies who recorded these balladeers, their sorrow was a platinum payoff, a jackpot of skulls crowned that particular week (the chart said) by Sinéad O'Connor's interpretation of "Nothing Compares 2 U." This, I told myself, was the first generation of compact discs: silver stacks minted to perform repeatedly, to spin eternally without distortion or diminishment; the voices encoded on them—the first sounds chosen for such preservation—shared a ubiquitous sadness that seemed to yearn for the gone days of vinyl, their voices plaintively aching to be abused once again with yesterday's needles.

Light from passing streetlamps skated over the oversized *Bill-*

board pages, dazzling the area that fell between the printed information and my own fickle attention. It was curious that dance
music seemed equally popular to this other sort, but what was
dance music, after all, but the affirmation of body magic and body
heat in the face of death? Wasn't this much the same outlet I once
sought from my misery by watching life and lust reaffirmed in
great pelvic thrusts on the screen at the Eros?

My cabbie, hearing that this was my first visit to the District,
was intent upon giving me the grand tour. He took me across
historic bridges, past famous landmarks, and maintained a running
monologue of the national secrets he had overheard from passengers while driving his hack. Any one of them, if true, was enough
to turn your hair white. I noticed that the words THE WAR had
been spray-painted onto every stop sign in town.

"After all, he was the Father of Our Country," the cabbie said,
his stock observation for the dramatic moment when the Washington Monument rose erectly into view. I ignored most of the
sights, familiar from postcards and television, attracted more by
the playful patterns of light on the open pages in my lap, remembering the similar patterns on our bedroom ceiling at night, as
Paige slept in my arms, when I couldn't sleep because something
unbidden was encroaching upon my mind.

Across from the chart that compiled the nation's Top Video
Rentals, *Billboard* ran a full-page ad—like an answer to the question posed by the world's record sales, the world's mood—for
Throat Sprockets. "By Popular Demand—Now on U.S. Videocassette."

To my astonishment the domestic tape release had entered the
charts at Number 3.

"You a married man?" the cabbie interrupted.

"Why do you ask?"

"Well, you hadn't said anything, so I figured maybe you was
shy or somethin'. Anyway"—he turned a corner before I could
read the street sign—"if you should happen to be in the mood for

a little company, this is where you'll find it," he said. "You're allowed to approach them but they can't approach you."

The streetwalkers stood in calculated groups of three, each trio encompassing a world of choice, a palette of pulchritude. They talked among themselves with their expressions caught by passing headlights in transient attitudes of sourness and passivity. Farther down the street one of the girls was leaning into the window of an idling limousine with midnight-blue windows; others paced back and forth from the corner in pairs like a human sandwich board, again deliberately composed of opposite types, promenading up and down the sidewalk in grand style, fleshy moves and fashion hooves. The lack of well-defined lighting on that side of the street probably worked to their benefit. I got a fairly good look at one of the girls, a Chinese in a magenta wig and spangled minidress, thin and probably heroin addicted, who stood bathed in the emerald neon light of a nearby bar; I suppose she had a beautiful mouth, but her throat looked rutted and rubbery, like a stalk of celery that's gone soft in an old Bloody Mary.

Things were more noticeable on the opposite side of the street, where an all-night coffee shop brightened half the block. The light streaming from its well-spaced windows made the hustlers over there easier to see, more attractive in a literal sense. If the right side of the street advertised female flesh in all its variety, the opposite side pandered to connoisseurs of youth. I couldn't quite believe my eyes; I didn't see anyone among them who appeared to be of legal age.

"What's this?" I asked. "Jail Bait Boulevard?"

The cabbie's eyes jumped to his rearview mirror and caught the direction in which I was looking. "You're casing the wrong side of the street, pal! You don't want that trash!"

"What do you mean?" I laughed. "What difference does it make, which side of the street I look at?"

"The difference is what side of *your* street you're looking at."

"I don't get you." I double-checked the way those young people were dressed, their demeanor of solicitation. "You're not saying those aren't hustlers?"

"Those are *chokers*," he clarified. "You don't want that trash!"

"I don't 'want' *any* of them," I protested. "What do you mean—'chokers'?"

He spoke over his shoulder, his eyes cautiously dodging between the dangers surrounding us on the road and gaining in number on the sidewalk on his side of the cab. "All right, cowboy, listen up. Chokers are *like* hookers, but use your eyes. They wear chokers on their necks—see? Those collar bands?"

"Yes. So?"

"Well, those chokers hide their marks. I hate to break it to you, mister, but there's enough sick assholes living here in the District to make becoming a walking blood bank profitable for a certain class of people. Sad thing is, it's probably safer than *boffin'* these days."

"You mean they let their . . . customers . . . *bite* them? But what about their blood? What about—?"

"AIDS?" He laughed. "Take a good look, man. You see anybody in that cattle call older than, say, seventeen? Eighteen, tops? Bunch o' runaways, most of 'em. Hated school, hated Mom, maybe Daddy Jim or Uncle Earl sat 'em on their lap once too often, who knows? There's a million stories in the naked city, as they say. But everybody walking that side of the street has a special commodity. You wanna guess?"

I bit my lip: abyss. "Virgin blood."

"Give the man a gold star. Just don't let any of 'em catch you look—aw, SHIT!" We jerked to a sudden halt, and the driver slapped the steering wheel with the butt of his hand. "Ain't that just my fuckin' luck!"

"What?"

"Aw, nothing," he said sarcastically, "not a thing! Just welcome to the longest red light in the District of Columbia, that's all."

There were at least four other cars between us and the intersection. There was a moment of absolute quiet—the kind of quiet that's never heard near any metropolitan intersection, no matter how late the hour—and then a sudden sound like heavy rain arose from my left. Only from my left.

"Roll up and lock up," I was ordered. "NOW!"

Within seconds a crowd of young girls and boys—the so-called "chokers"—swarmed into the street to encircle the vehicles stalled by the red light, pressing their hands and faces against the glass of the taxi, faces formerly anonymous with distance, now sufficiently close to bring the horror of their individual situations into sharp focus. They were kids, just kids and, like anything, potentially dangerous in strong numbers. I did as I was told, cranking my window shut against a sea of chiding and aggression.

Some of the chokers stank of bubble gum, others wore candy necklaces. The boys were skinny and unsophisticated, wearing black T-shirts and jeans, with western-style kerchiefs about their throats; most of the girls wore their inexperience on their sleeves as well, their acne miserably disguised with makeup. Their bumpy cheeks were too pink, the shadings above their eyes too pronounced, applied in volume and haste. They were young, hungry, and probably homeless, the lot of them, vitamin-deficient beings renting themselves out as nourishment, colt awkward, branded. For the length of that red light I was their pet, their squirming tropical fish.

"Don't pretend, lover—we saw you looking," one taunted.

"Lover? You mean 'Glover,' don't you?" leered another.

"You can't fool us!"

"Back off, bitches," one of the boys warned. He fought through the crowd to fawn at my window. "He likes a little stubble in his nibble, if you ask me."

"I'm Type A positive," offered another girl, tiptoeing to look over the heads of those in front of her. "That means I'm *rare*—you asshole!"

That did it: the girl's obscenity somehow snapped the slender thread of propriety that had held them back until it was uttered. At that very moment the chokers began pummeling the taxi with their fists, then with their cheap dime-store purses, their sweaty palms, their Woolworth's heels. The cab began to rock.

"C'mon—do something," I urged the driver, holding on.

The driver was staring back at the red signal, swaying in the sky, holding sway. "Change, you fucker, *change*," he growled at the mechanism. "God *damn* you!"

"I thought you said they couldn't *approach* us," I yelled.

"I said *bookers* couldn't," he yelled back. "Hang on, pal! D.C. tactics comin' up!"

Before I could grasp the warning, I was sent sprawling across the backseat in the direction opposite his wrenching of the steering wheel, crumpling the *Billboard* magazine. There was a muffled thump outside, and we huddled away through the narrow aisle between two lanes of immobile traffic. I thought I heard a voice in the distance scream, "Pez Boy! They hit Pez Boy!"

The driver rolled down his window and jeered into our wake, "What's the matter, you buncha babies? Can't you handle the sight of a little *blood?*"

Then, reeling his window shut with one hand, he slapped his turn signal with the other to merge with a desired lane. Our sealed vehicle soon smelled of sweat and anxiety, intimacy of a kind. I looked out the rear window of the cab where, about a block away, I could see the fellow called Pez Boy being helped to his feet, evidently shaken but otherwise uninjured. The light must have changed, because we then reentered the flow of traffic and moved on, the episode receding until it was swallowed by the lengths and turns of city blocks.

I didn't turn to face the front again until I had started to regain some composure, half expecting with each corner we turned that a crowd of massive proportions would turn the corner moments after us, a club-bearing tide of humanity.

"Fuckin' hemos," the cabbie muttered.

Another town, another hotel, another green-foiled mint on my pillow. Welcome, traveler: suck on this.

• • •

That evening in Washington was mine to do with as I wished. Unwilling to leave my hotel room to encounter the downstairs feeding frenzy head-on, I called Emma and spent an hour listening to her voice, then spent a few hours sketching boards for the next morning's presentation; afterward, I sought to distract myself from my thoughts by reading the entertainment menu for TV options. A number of pay-per-view titles were listed, including—I can't honestly say I was surprised—*Throat Sprockets*. Although I felt a powerful temptation to access the film, I decided to do without it, the fantasy it afforded now fully realized in my relationship with Emma; I was also, I should admit, mildly concerned that an independent viewing might inspire me to stray, to request one of those undernourished but quite nourishing children of the night from room service. No. No no no no no. I stuck with the free channels.

The local news channels were reporting the story of a rich kid who had committed suicide in Los Angeles by jumping off a Sunset Strip billboard advertising a soon-to-be-released motion picture, but no one—presumably at the studio's urging—was saying or showing *which* billboard. The story was being glossed over by CNN and the network affiliates, in favor of the Middle East crisis. The local independent stations offered a toss-up between a Burt Reynolds movie (edited for television) and a syndicated program called *Direct Current*.

Direct Current was staged in a small studio to a live audience of fewer than a hundred people, most of them teenage males in AXL RULES T-shirts with a predisposition to whoaing and hooting. The host baited the throng every way he knew how, punctuating his tart delivery with tough sucks on a cigarette. The camera pulled back from the host to encompass a view of two guests—male and female—standing at opposite podiums, emblazoned with the *Di-*

rect Current logo: an open mouth with a jagged lightning bolt tongue zapping out.

AUDIENCE: HOO HOO HOO HOO HOO . . .

HOST: Zip it! Let's hear what Mr. Anonymous here has to say. *[To MAN at podium]* Go on, pal—you were saying?

The man at the podium appeared to be in his middle twenties. What might have seemed like pride at a distance was, under closer scrutiny, a humid stance of public nervousness and deep personal concerns. His hair was perhaps too well cut for him to be considered trustworthy among his own age group, and he was much better dressed than his boorish jurors.

MAN: You're all making it sound sick, like it's some kind of violence. But it's not. It's . . . how can I describe it? It's a moment of danger that functions as a test of courage and a demonstration of love that's actually kind of tender. I mean, anybody can **** anybody, right? What's the big deal there? A lot of people go around screwing people they don't know and probably won't ever see again. But how many lovers do you have in your lifetime who you would trust to hold your very life between their teeth?

HOST: *[Splutters]* How many? I'll tell you how many, sucker! A big, fat ZERO—*that's* how many!

AUDIENCE: HOO HOO HOO HOO HOO . . .

MAN: I'm sorry to hear that, because it's not just an offering of affection. It's the validation of that affection.

AUDIENCE: HOO HOO HOO HOO HOO . . .

HOST: Very . . . very . . . *[To AUDIENCE]* Hey, zip it up there! *[To MAN, condescendingly]* Very eloquent, kid. Very eloquent. But can I just share a little thought with you?

MAN: Sure, if you can spare it.

HOST: *[Smirks dangerously]* I just want to say this. *[With rising anger, prodding MAN with the two fingers clenching his cigarette]* If you're, if you're as friend-less as that attitude of yours ought to make you, I suggest you get on the horn to the folks over at 1-800-976-NAZI! 'Cause Hitler could use an ******** like you for his own personal speech-writer!

The host exited the shot in triumph, his spectators roaring with gorilla approval.

AUDIENCE: HOO HOO HOO HOO HOO . . .

MAN: Well, that just goes to show—

HOST: *[Interrupting MAN]* Zip it!

MAN: —how out of touch you are with the world, man, 'cause Hitler's—

HOST: *[Interrupting again]* I told you to zip it! So zip it!

MAN: He's been dead for over forty years!

The host staggered backward like a court jester, the palms of his hands held upward as if juggling two colossal balls. The man at the podium reacted, his expression souring, as if clearly pained by the exhibition.

HOST: That's right, that's right! And every time some sick bastard like you has the big brass balls to stand at a public podium and spout off the steamiest pile of horse**** anyone's likely to find outside a skinhead rally, THAT is when decent, clean-living men and women—like the decent, clean-living men and women of my audience—

AUDIENCE: HOO HOO HOO HOO HOO . . .

HOST: —that's when we find ourselves reminded of that bloodthirsty sonofabitch all over again!

AUDIENCE: HOO HOO HOO HOO HOO . . .

The host waved his fist in a pitcher's windup motion of encouragement, keeping the hoots of the crowd coming. I thought of my cabbie, winding up his window against a tide of human merchandise. This was followed by a close shot of the woman at the second podium, who had not as yet spoken. She wore her dark hair short and was slightly older than the male guest, perhaps in her late thirties. She wore a choker on her neck, but there was no mistaking it as a point of allure. She seemed to wear it as a gesture of defiance. The host swaggered into frame.

HOST: *[To WOMAN at 2nd podium]* Yes, ma'am. Folks, this is Harry Anna Fellini—

WOMAN: *[Correcting HOST]* Ariana.

HOST: Oh, excuse me! "Awry Awna" Fellini, a recovered sprocketee who has a point she'd like to make. You any relation to that filmmaker Fellini, Awry Awna?

WOMAN: No.

HOST: Jeez, y'know, I saw that movie of his, 8½. Oh, man! I guess if a movie stinks like a sweatsock, you name it after a shoe size, right? Okay, so what's on your mind, babe?

WOMAN: I just have one thing to say.

HOST: Go ahead.

WOMAN: And that's that some men will dream up anything to avoid having to look straight into a woman's eyes and having to deal with her as a real individual!

HOST: Ouch! Where have we heard that before, eh? [To MAN at podium] Well, whaddya say to that . . . BELA?

AUDIENCE: HOO HOO HOO HOO HOO . . .

MAN: I'd like—I say, I would like to respond to that. I said, if the crowd would just pipe down a minute, I'd like to respond to that.

AUDIENCE: HOO HOO HOO HOO HOO . . .

MAN: I'd like to respond to that, if I may?

HOST: [To AUDIENCE] Zip it! [AUDIENCE calms down] Hitler speaks.

AUDIENCE: [With renewed enthusiasm] HOO HOO HOO HOO HOO . . .

It took at least forty to fifty seconds, and some meagerly conciliatory "simmer down" motions from the host's conductive hand, for the throng to regain its composure. The male guest dragged his fingers through his hair in exasperation and embarked on his statement.

MAN: All right. What I want to say is, the fact that I'm a throat fetishist has not seriously interfered with the way in which I form or maintain relationships with the opposite sex. On the contrary—

WOMAN: *[Interrupting]* Of course it hasn't! According to statistics there are about thirty female masochists out there for every male with serious sadistic tendencies! The odds are somewhat in your favor, I would say.

HOST: Hoo boy! Did you say thirty female masochists for every male with serious sadistic tendencies?

WOMAN: Yes, I think the statistics will bear me out on that.

HOST: Jesus! Whatever happened to "Two girls for every boy," huh?

MAN: I'd like to see those statistics.

WOMAN: I'm sure that's not all you'd like to see.

AUDIENCE: HOO HOO HOO HOO HOO . . .

As the woman continued speaking, she reached vaguely for her choker as if to reassure an old wound that it was safe.

WOMAN: Our society is a veritable breeding ground for women who are victimized, who are taught to be victimized, who want to be victimized, and who ritually thwart their own opportunities for happiness!

MAN: For God's sake, this is a *personal* issue, not a societal issue!

HOST: OhYESitis, ohYESitis! Listen up for a minute, everybody. Let me just tell you something, okay? The weather's finally starting to warm up a bit, but did any of you get away from your TVs long enough this winter to get a good look at the snow this year? Let me just say this. Our parking lot's about a block away from the studio and I walk here, five nights a week. With two off for good behavior, right? And I'm walking to the studio in the snow and looking down at my Totes galoshes, you know? And, hey, I walk through the same snow as anybody else. I see the yellow stains and the occasional brown stuff and, every once in a while, I see a, you know, a little rubber thing in there. *[Races across the stage, grabs MAN by the lapels]* But this is the first winter I've ever seen RED snow, man! You and your loathsome kind, you parade around— calling yourselves fetishists! But in my book, Mr. Worm, Mr. Scumbag, Mr. **********, Mr. Anonymous, Mr. Nobody, Mr. Dip****, you're nothing but a worthless, disgusting, no-good . . . NAPIST!

AUDIENCE: HOO HOO HOO HOO HOO . . .

Having achieved the desired effect the Host abruptly dropped his frightened guest's lapels. As the man smoothed them with his hands, the host turned to the camera with a broad, theatrical grin —the emotional opposite of where he was only seconds ago.

HOST: Tonight's topic: THROAT SPROCKETS— America's latest indoor sport! What won't these sick ****s think up next? C'mon back!

At this the camera cut to the program's main titles, a cheaply animated color Xerox sequence that culminated in the *Direct Current* logo shown on the podiums. However, in deference to the subject matter at hand, the mouth's bared upper incisors had been exaggerated by the station's art department into fangs and viewers were encouraged to dial 1-800-976-BITE.

• • •

It was my purpose in town to show the Consolations people my ideas for their domestic (print and billboard) and international (television) advertisements. At nine-fifteen the following morning I met with their vice-president in charge of advertising for a private chat, preliminary to our scheduled ten o'clock conference. "Coffin" Niles Rodriguez was a tall and distinguished-looking Latino whose broad shoulders and narrowing figure did indeed suggest a coffin; his expression was careworn, and his still-dark hair had receded on either side of a pronounced widow's peak. An attentive man, he deduced from my eyes that I had slept little and kindly had an associate wheel a coffee service into our briefing.

"Big emotions," I explained apologetically, handing him my leather portfolio case. He unzipped it with elegant haste.

"I see," he purred, flipping through the boards. "You have provided more than one option here," he noted.

"At SPI we believe in the value of the original idea and have no use for committee thinking. That isn't to say that we don't believe in coverage. All of the boards before you are mine. The choice is yours."

Rodriguez handled the boards with regard and suavity, his arm draped behind them as if wrapped around the back of a dancing partner. I drank one coffee quickly, gratefully, then a second with more deliberation, all the while rocking my foot to an imaginary accompaniment. After admiring my own personal preferences and one or two alternatives, he mentioned that there was an associate who maybe ought to be in on this, and pressed his intercom.

"Yes?" it said.

"Lynn, I'm looking at some *fantastic* pictures in here. Would you buzz Nancy Reagan and ask her to join us, please?"

Catching my reaction from the corner of his eye, "Coffin" Niles smiled broadly and reassured me, "No, not *that* Nancy Reagan."

• • •

First billboard: a male model in the foreground cups his hands to light a cigarette against the night wind; in the background a woman can be seen walking away toward an illuminated city skyline. WHEN YOU FEAR YOU'VE LOST HER . . . CONSOLATIONS.

Second billboard: the same male model is seated alone at a bar, looking introspective, pensively smoking a cigarette; all around him, like an ectoplasmic haze, is the face of a beautiful woman. WHEN YOU CAN'T GET HER OUT OF YOUR MIND . . . CONSOLATIONS.

Third billboard: the model's right hand rests against the glassy dome of a jukebox—hundreds of songs listed on metal pages inside—with a cigarette clamped between two fingers, while his left hand hesitates above the selection buttons. WHEN EVERY SONG REMINDS YOU OF HER . . . CONSOLATIONS.

I had drawn other boards along similar lines—all of them inspired by the pain of separation I was experiencing—but it was agreed among the board of directors that this particular sequence told the best story.

"What I find irresistible about this concept is how nothing in these boards is more individually important than the element that's *missing* from them," Niles stated, seated at the head of the conference table.

"Exactly," someone echoed. "The void. The void felt at times by every consumer. The void that says, 'Buy.' It suggests Consolations as a kind of pacifier against the universal void."

"You're right, Niles; they're stunning," Nancy Reagan announced. Then she looked at me quite directly and said, with an irony discernible to only the two of us, "I wonder where he gets such ideas."

"Hey, write that down, somebody," said another.

"What?" asked someone with a pencil.

"Pacifiers. Run a copyright check, then add it to the names we're testing for that new budget brand. No no, wait! Make that *Pacifier*—in the French style!"

The board of directors felt that I had found the special identity that their product so desperately needed; it was decided that these advertisements would go into the earliest possible release, dominating highway billboards coast to coast, where they would be replaced every four months with new copy. Niles treated me and several other members of the Consolations team to dinner that night. Nancy Reagan sought to make eye contact with me throughout the meal and, after an hour of polite resistance, actually followed me into the men's room.

"Bump bump, you old cherry picker," she teased, playfully flexing her *sternocleidomastoideus,* as she had in the old days.

I zipped up and explained that I was flattered—but attached.

"You were attached *then,*" she said.

"Sort of," I admitted. "I was getting over a divorce."

"Oh?" She lit a cigarette. She held it out to me, wet tipped; I didn't take it. "So who's the new girlfriend?"

"She's—everything I could possibly want."

Nancy blew some smoke above my head and gave me one of those green, peering, sizing-up looks of hers. "She must be a real movie star," she snorted, as she turned and walked out.

I left the restaurant knowing that I would return to Friendship the next day with a three-year contract in my portfolio case, ripe for Austin's signature. And that my attachment to Emma was much stronger than I had realized.

• • •

Back at my Hay-Adams hotel room I turned off the television and stood for several long minutes at the window, fourteen floors above the street, looking down on anonymous cars, taxis, and limos being harassed as they sped through gauntlets of anonymous virgins. I reflected on the period of my own virginity, which

I hadn't lost until my eighteenth year (rather late for someone of my generation), remembering how deeply I had felt its disadvantages. Now that I had amassed a proper perspective, I realized that it had actually been an advantage; to lose my chastity in marriage, to someone I truly loved, had been the blessing of my life. I would never again feel anything so meaningful, so well distributed throughout my mind and body, as I had felt my covenant with Paige. Every awareness or sensation that I had known since, no matter how gratifying in its immediacy, was fundamentally misdirected; I was fucking with my brain and thinking with my belly. *A form of arousal that seems to encompass the higher self, a lust so new that it feels like a form of enlightenment, consigning the brain's former responsibilities to the unthinking, uncensored, primal regions of the gut,* to quote the fork in the road. The path I had chosen had twisted everything all around. Now I had seen the faces of those lost souls at first hand: inexperienced children, whose eyes had seen everything, whose heads were too constipated with dreams of security to consider the matter of their own safety, and on whose throats the unredeemable ticket to those dreams was worn. A price tag.

Dark thoughts converging, I called Emma so that her voice might drown them out. She assured me that I was not alone and read to me from a book of Shakespeare until I fell fast asleep.

4

Where you came from is gone, where you thought you were going to never was there, and where you are is no good unless you can get away from it.

Flannery O'Connor
Wise Blood

ONCE UPON A TIME IN THE WEST

AND THEN THERE WAS THE TIME—NOT THE FIRST, AND CERTAINLY NOT the last night I cried for having met her—I waited for news of Emma in a Los Angeles emergency ward.

We had been seeing one another for about a year, and we were visiting the City of Angels to test our compatibility with the projected home-base for the West Coast branch of SPI, the command of which the Old Man had implicitly offered to me. Emma was willing to relocate to California, to invade Rodeo Drive with her exclusive line of long-necked vases. The question was, did we really want to pack our bags with real things and move to the Land of Illusion?

"Try it for a spell," Austin had said, tossing me the keys to his Malibu retreat.

I gazed through tears and an observatory window at the LA night, thinking to myself that it looked like a very expensive matte painting . . . but, of course, it *was* a very expensive matte painting. In the foreground of the winter cityscape was a billboard for *Throat Sprockets*—this month, exclusively on Cinemax. The movie that I had always considered mine alone had never truly been mine alone; I reflected back on the dramatically increased attendance at the Eros on the last night *Throat Sprockets* had played there, and this was all the proof I needed that none of the terror spreading through the real world was solely my fault. Of course, the other billboards within easy view—for Necromancer, TV Heaven, and Consolations—suggested that I wasn't entirely innocent, either, but I was surrounded in Hollywood by nameless people who were responsible, in one way or another, for billboards whose influence had reshaped the reality of all fifty states into a configuration more suitable and profitable for their faceless interests. Out west the sense of blame was positively chummy, and this relieved everyone's sense of culpability. Things were monstrous in Los Angeles, but this was somehow acceptable because, within the city's capacity for monstrousness and its potentiality for melodrama, was the unscripted grist of unproduced films. Whatever happens, however terrible—the local wisdom went—I can use that. It was my intuition that horror films were on the verge of a big comeback.

Emma convinced me to finally accept a Necromancer LTD from Lee Torrence and Maverick Motors, and chauffeured me around the city in this brand-new bloodred status symbol. With her at the wheel I was able to barrel down those winding hillside roads riding shotgun, watching bizarre movies speeding past my passenger window. Virtually every building on every street had appeared in at least one film or television show I had seen. Driving through Los Angeles was like driving through a 3D movie, and thanks to the smog, driving caused the same kind of headaches and eyestrain. With car chases and crashes so popular in films, I wasn't surprised at the number of actual car accidents I witnessed in the course of a week; I noticed a particular tendency to accelerate through stoplights. I saw it happen again from the observatory window as if, everywhere at once, the color red was becoming confused with an encouragement to GO.

GO FOR THE THROAT, as my current Necromancer campaign advised.

Those four words could be seen sparkling from billboards up and down Sunset and La Cienega, and I remembered while pacing about the waiting area that my next set of Consolations billboards would soon be due in Washington. I composed them on the spot:

WHEN THE DOCTOR ASKS YOU TO TAKE A SEAT . . . CONSOLATIONS.

WHEN THERE'S NOTHING LEFT TO DO BUT WAIT . . . CONSOLATIONS.

WHEN IT'S NOT MANLY TO WEEP . . . CONSOLATIONS.

• • •

The world had changed a lot in a year. The domestic release of *Throat Sprockets* on videocassette catapulted behavior that had been reasonably circumspect during its theatrical run and import days into mainstream visibility. Like most erotic indulgences sprocketing did not look quite as transcendent in a bedroom mirror as it did on film, or behind a participant's closed eyes. It was not long after my trip to Washington, where I had made its acquaintance at first hand, that the word *choker* first invaded newspaper headlines. A young runaway from Grand Rapids, Michigan, had died in a tragic miscalculation, apparently while prostituting himself to the wealthy tenant of a Manhattan penthouse. In the wake of this private disaster and its worldwide publicity, some *Throat Sprockets* cultists who were more candid or flaunting about their life-style than myself were denounced by politicians as pornographers and worse. Feminist groups rallied to condemn sprocketing as the most outrageous expression to date of violence against women. A renowned sociologist described sprocketing as symptomatic of the fractured emotions of media-disoriented people—an act that was "not only impersonal and irresponsible, but fearfully antisexual in its fervid determination to eroticize obscene ugliness." Another public speaker with roots in the Christian community jumped past all that mumbo-jumbo and declaimed the practice as a cancer, pure and simple, eating away at that approved backbone of society, the American family. Other pompous prognosticators, speaking on the Lord's behalf, claimed that what began in pornography would surely end in the flames of

Hell, that the satanic zeal of the sprocketeers could harvest nothing less than the very spores of Armageddon. It was from this corner that a Christian extremist organization called STOKER—the Society To Obliterate Kinky Erotic Recreation—arose; it was from its members that defamatory words like *vampire* were first uttered, spreading like a brushfire from their prayer meetings to the covers of supermarket tabloids, to the headlines of the nation's great newspapers, into presidential press conferences and *Tonight Show* monologues. Emma and I referred to this rising tide of intolerance, between ourselves, as "blood pressure."

It was also a favorite claim of critics that sprocketing—as a form of erotic behavior with no place in the scheme of human reproduction—was, like masturbation or fellatio or anal intercourse, an essentially selfish and therefore promiscuous act. This wasn't true, and fuck them if it was. Speaking for myself, the impossible erotic tensions I had once felt in the presence of bare-throated women, or women in turtleneck sweaters, completely subsided once I had found someone with whom I could release them, and Emma and I happily entered into a kind of monogamy that would have put half the world's heterogenital relationships to statistical shame. Of course, I continued to notice other women, as have billions of happily married men in the course of human history. As I explained to my mate, bitterly twisting the parlance of common prejudice to my own advantage, "I may be a *vampire*—but I'm not a corpse!"

I can speak only for myself: I was never motivated by a thirst for blood, nor was I, in any way, sexually aroused by making Emma bleed; that was our moment of climax, if you will, the sign that our carnal tensions had been released and relaxed. I drank her yield as often as I did not, just as other acts of oral lovemaking involve swallowing as often as not, and the decision to do, or not to do, did nothing to make the act itself more or less pleasurable for myself or my partner. It was, each time out, a curve navigated on impulse.

I would have done anything for her, but Emma never expressed an interest in reversing our roles by sprocketing me. It would have been somehow contrary to the film in which we felt ourselves wedded, perverted the heightened sensations she felt from giving. Not that the examples set down by the film were strictly observed by every couple; *Throat Sprockets* contained no homosexual episodes, but I occasionally saw men wearing ascots and turtlenecks on the streets of Friendship, and such accoutrements proved even more popular among men in the larger cities we saw on television, observed in the backgrounds of related news stories breaking in London, New York, or San Francisco. The turtleneck and ascot were assuming their place among the other fashion communiqués of contemporary gay culture, newborn nouns in the secret language of the back-pocket handkerchief, the pack of cigarettes worn in the roll of a sleeve, and the black leather wristband. Such clearly marked targets were easy prey for the guns of judgment.

In the midst of this political climate Emma and I had sensed that our newfound Eden was succumbing to dusk. In our determination to dissociate ourselves from the mirror being rudely held up to our ways in the streets and on nightly television, we sought to redefine who we were. In the desperation to remain together, pure and undefiled, our mutual pleasures experimentally branched out into related but alternative directions.

Like the belly-button episode.

Like her dream.

• • •

I had returned that night to Malibu to find the place empty, the mirror-topped table in the Old Man's video room overturned. As I stood it back on its legs, I caught signs of violence on the patio and was seized with concern that Emma had left me. The red eye on the answering machine blinked with messages. There were the expected calls from Austin and Nancy and Austin and Austin, but the most important message had been left by a staff physician at a nearby hospital:

"Hello, this is Dr. Allcome calling. Could you please come as soon as possible to our emergency ward?" He explained that Emma was being hospitalized for reasons that would be disclosed to me at the hospital; she was in serious but stable condition. "Oh, yes," he continued, "I'm afraid her clothing had to be torn to administer treatment. Would you please bring her a change of clothes? Just give my name to the front desk. Thank you." Click.

I grabbed a pair of jeans and a green sweatshirt from the closet, wondering what could have happened and imagining the worst, picturing the clothes in my arms soaked through with violet-black blood. Not quite trusting myself after so much time to handle a car, I ran all the way to the hospital. The emergency ward was almost surreally vacant. Breathlessly, I announced myself at the information desk, where an attractive nurse with milk-white skin relieved me of Emma's clothing. She invited me to take a seat in the waiting area down the hall, in the room beside the observatory. I would be summoned when Dr. Allcome was ready to see me.

There was a love seat with vanilla vinyl cushions near the window, where I took my place. There were four different waiting areas in the ward, one in each bend of its corridors, each of them unoccupied. From the love seat I could see the main desk, where two other nurses were chatting and drinking coffee. Their telephone rang, but they sank the receiver back into its cradle with haste, suggesting a wrong number. After a few moments one of them turned in my direction and started walking toward me, and I was concerned that the foil-bright green lettering on their computer screen had borne bad news. This nurse—a brunette who approximated my type so closely that I nearly mistook her for Emma or someone more to the point—spoke my name from the far end of the corridor, then slowly approached me. We had not yet spoken, so I instinctively reached out and shook her hand. We laughed a bit nervously, there being no set formalities for such situations.

"It's going to be a long night," she said. "We have a fresh pot of coffee at the desk, if that sounds good to you."

"Thank you, yes, it does."

"You don't look to me like the cream-and-sugar type."

"I'm not, no."

I started to follow her back to the desk, but she quickly gestured for me to remain. "Stay put, I'll get it; it gives me something to do."

Moments later, I sipped the black coffee, as I watched the nurse saunter back to her post in cream-colored stockings. Time continued to pass without an explanation of the harm that had befallen Emma. I ransacked my memories of our encounter that morning, which had been remarkable mostly for her almost complete lack of interest. Watching the nurse's shapely legs as they sauntered away, I asked myself why my fetish couldn't have been something innocent—like white stockings? Wanting them . . . becoming fixated on their seminal sheen . . . or being tied up with them . . . hell, liking to wear them . . . *anything*, instead of . . .

• • •

Her eyes were dead, but her voice was Born Again. I heard it again like the narration of another missing scene. The Waiting Room Scene.

Baby, I had The Most Amazing Dream.

I wasn't in it. But you were.

You were in a strange hospital, pacing around. You were waiting for word about me. It must have been me, because you were as upset about it as if something bad had happened to you.

Our phone rang in the middle of the night and I wasn't there and you ran all the way, just to be with me. In my hospital room I could feel you— through my sedation—running to me, coming to me, all the way from clear across town.

The halls in the emergency ward were mostly empty, as happens only in dreams.

You waited ever so long, but then a doctor came to show you how to find me.

He escorted you deep inside the bowels of the hospital to a place where all the halls were dark. You cursed to keep your courage up.

You walked on and on, until the doctor said that you were now entering the ward where the Operations of the Unconscious were performed.

The numbers on the patients' doors hovered in the darkness with an almost visceral significance.

The doctor wanted to put you at your ease, knowing that you needed all your strength for the test you were about to face. So he decided to tell you about some of the patients in this special ward. Like the woman who'd had her living body mummified in the veins of a married man she'd loved long from afar.

He told you they'd done it for her because she was the friend of a friend. . . .

Then he brought you to a very special room. The number on that door was especially familiar, resonating in your nerves and sinews like your first kiss. And then you understood the significance of the number, which was not only the number on the room in this most unusual hospital wing, but also the number on the house where we were living together. Yes, dear: in this dream, we lived together.

You looked at the number and said, "Small world." But then, almost right away, you understood that it wasn't a small world, not really.

It's just that God is looking after fewer people.

• • •

I awoke with a curse, hot coffee stinging my leg; exhaustion and sleep had snatched me away before I could put my cup down. I dashed to the men's room at the end of the corridor, around the corner from the main desk, where the nurses snickered at my four-letter outburst, and applied cold water to dissolve the stain. I turned off the tap a minute later and heard the hollow acoustics of the tiled rest room intermittently punched by heavy male sobs from a closed stall.

I was sitting on the vanilla vinyl cushions of the love seat once again, stroking my chinos where they hadn't stained, thinking of Emma. I felt I had done a terrible injustice to this woman—with whom I had shared an endlessly repeated ritual, outside of which we now barely existed as friends—and done equal damage to the other half of myself, the half that had been my wife, with whom only that one, small form of expression had been impossible. For the taste of a little blood, I had thrown away an entire heart.

I heard the nurse's soft white shoes walking toward me again. I thought she was going to offer me a warm-up, but by the time she stood before me, brunette and sullen, I realized that she was in fact the other nurse on duty.

"Looks like it's going to be a long night," she announced. "I was going to make a run to the cafeteria. Is there anything I can get for you?"

I was resisting food. Hunger, the deprivation of oral instincts, was becoming a friend. Somehow I felt the fact of hunger exposing my nerve ends, bringing me closer to the sensation of living.

"No, thanks," I said. "Is there any word yet about—"

"No, I'm afraid not."

"Is there an update yet on her condition? When can I see her?"

"You would have to ask a doctor or nurse about that, sir."

"But aren't you a nurse?"

"Only some of the time," she smiled, positioning herself before the view of the Hollywood hills. "To tell you the truth, I'm really an actress."

•   •   •

The doctor opened the door that bore our number.

The two of you proceeded into a room where everything was as white as a wedding. You reached for your eyes to protect them from the light, or perhaps to hide your tears. There are times, I suppose, when it's not manly to weep.

The doctor guided you by the arm to the beautiful bed where I was at rest.

Perhaps in the dream I was seeing myself for the first time through your eyes: I looked so becalmed, so clear and beautiful, that the menace underlying the mystery levitated right out of the dream. Is that really how you see me?

You held my hands and looked so happy to find me there, at the center of all that mystery, after all the horrible waiting you'd gone through, after running all the way across town, just to be with me—that you actually did weep.

All my colors ran together in your tears.

I let go of your hands and began to unfasten the lace bow at my throat. The doctor left us alone. From that moment on, nothing existed outside our mutual glow.

I undid the front of my gown.

I reached past my breasts to the center of my chest, and opened it to you like a pair of golden cupboard doors.

The light of the room touched me inside, where light had never touched. My heart was beating inside, and I invited you without words, with only a smile, to take it. To hold it. . . .

I looked like a Madonna. My smile seemed to say, Take this, for everything I have given to you has started here, is most potent here. Everything I shall ever give you will come from here, where it is now being generated. The love we share is secreted here, wept from here, pumped from here. I want to feel the prize of our love in your hands, to entrust it to your hands.

Your hands extended into the light and the dream closed around my face, like an iris shot from a silent film. All I could see was the light of my smile, my perfectly happy smile . . . my perfect contentment . . . beaming down on you like heavenly grace. . . .

I've never seen such love.

I've never known such love.

I want to, though.

• • •

I am not alone in cherishing certain dreams of an erotic nature that I know to be impossible. On the contrary, is there anyone who doesn't hoard and nurture a secret dream within a dream? Do we not always find ourselves returning in our thoughts to the same ecstasy, like a token unredeemed, its animation forever suspended in the tender parts of our bodies, a yearning idealized by the very principle that it must never happen, must remain forever beyond enacting—unspoken—because of who we are, because of who we have become in relation to our loved ones? For the sworn monogamist this dilemma may be nearly as vast as the opposite sex. A racist may burn with sweet curiosity about the skins of races beyond his tolerance. Or a man without children may obsess that he will, in all likelihood, die without ever knowing the taste of a woman's milk. These things are as dark and unspeakable as they are human, these things to do with being alive and under sentence of death and wanting no corner of gainful human experience to escape us.

It was in this spirit that Emma had confided her dream to me. Though my first impulse after hearing this fantasy was to feel sickened, I could tell that it excited her terribly; I could even taste the excitement brought on by these images, an adrenaline tang in the blood she imparted as, over and over again, she confided her dream to me like a vision of a distant land.

"Isn't it beautiful?" she would ask, out of nowhere.

Though the subject had been nowhere near our topic of conversation or the quiet at hand, I would know exactly what she meant.

"I don't know," I would tell her, in all honesty. "All that red."

"Blood is bluish till it comes in contact with air. Then it turns red. You can only see it blue on film."

"In blue movies," I would joke. "Seriously, it sounds so messy. Blood is one thing, but—*organs*? I don't know. What if I got sick?"

"You didn't see it the way I did, Angel Face." Several minutes to a quarter of an hour would pass, and then she would speculate, "I wonder how we could make it happen."

"My God, would you really want to? Imagine the pain—if not during, then afterward. The steel sutures, the afterburn of tho-

racic invasion. Some people take their lives after open-heart surgery, you know. It's a deeply disturbing procedure."

"It would be different with us," she would say, as blithely as if it
had already happened. "Those poor people have open heart surgery because they *have* to, not because they *want* to. I wouldn't
mind the pain. Really! I mean, it hurts me every time we sprocket,
but that's my gift to you. But to literally give you my heart? That's
a supreme gift. It's incontestable love. You should have seen my
face. I've never seen such love. I've never *known* such love. I *want*
to, though."

Then she turned toward me and said, in a disturbingly formal
voice, "Dr. Allcome will see you now . . ."

• • •

The nurse leaned a little closer, buffering her disruption with
intimacy. The space between us was scratched and speckled like
celluloid in motion.

"I'm sorry to disturb you, sir, but Dr. Allcome will see you
now."

Dr. Allcome was a bag-faced man in his late sixties who wore
dark glasses indoors, even in darkened rooms, as if to shield his
identity. He looked up from Emma's case study—which I mistook
at first for a screenplay—and motioned for me to sit.

"Let me understand this," I stammered from his chair, after
hearing a partial explanation. "She was attacked? Assaulted right
there on the patio, in the open?"

"That is correct."

"Doctor," I hedged, after a few moments of absorptive silence,
"during her preliminary examination certain markings on her
body must have been noticed. Near her throat?"

Allcome murmured in the affirmative.

"Well, I just wanted to make sure that you understand that
those are not exactly injuries. . . . I mean, I'm sure you'll understand my concern, when I tell you . . ."

Allcome's chin puckered, the only part of his face that registered visible skepticism. "I recognized immediately the nature of those markings, young man. Please understand that I'm not here to judge you, nor am I permitted to inform those who would."

"When can I see her?" I asked.

"Not for a while," Allcome said. "She's being prepped for OR."

"*Surgery?* Is that really necessary?"

"I'm afraid that is something only surgery can tell us," he explained.

I was able to picture the look on her face as her attackers descended on the patio, almost as if I had been there; it was the force of my love, my empathy. "She's not really like that, Doctor," I eventually said. "It's me. I can't help it, but she's trying her best to, I don't know . . ."

"Wean you?"

"I suppose so. When we do it anymore, it's like—it's like she's somewhere else, like she isn't even there. I think she's moving toward something else."

"Does that frighten you?"

"Sometimes."

"What frightens you?"

I want to, though.

"She says she wants to give me her heart."

The doctor smiled knowingly. "You know, they say that Ulysses was a great adventurer. A real hero, Ulysses; Kirk Douglas played him in the movies. He sailed the globe and dallied for seven years on the isle of the sea nymph Calypso, where he enjoyed the immortality of an image captured on film; he plundered and blinded the Cyclops; he partook of the lotus, whose fragrance made him forgetful of his home, and battled vicious man-eating tribes and saw his crew reduced around him to gibbering swine; he had himself tied to his ship's mast so that he could resist the dolorous song of the Sirens; and for most of his earthly years he left his home defenseless and his wife without a husband. The time comes in every adventure when a man must ask himself if he is embracing the unknown because he cannot face the known. Ulysses was willing to go to Hades before he was willing to go home.

"Some free advice. Don't be afraid of intimacy, son."

Allcome walked me back to the love seat in the waiting area, then continued on down the hall, butting through two swinging doors that bore the red-lettered advisory DO NOT ENTER.

• • •

My brain was soft, overburdened with images, soggy with too many lessons learned with too little effort. My reliance on pictures had been going on for so long—and I, in turn, felt so implicated in the foisting of this image scam on the outside world—that I had become estranged from any information that didn't dance before my eyes of its own accord. I seemed to recall myself, in another lifetime, as a reader of books, but I had subsisted for a couple of years on nothing more literate or objective than my own billboards.

The waiting room offered few distractions (television, window, clock, magazines) from the passing hours, and there were few others to be found elsewhere in the ward (other windows, nurses, the open doors of patients' rooms, other clocks). My withdrawal from words barred me from thumbing through the magazines fanned on the end tables, but the desperation of empty hours and empty hands—and the literary resonance of Allcome's Homeric advice—made them appear more and more enticing.

I decided to flip through one or two, or more if necessary, simply looking at the pictures; that would help to pass the time. *Time*, in fact, was the most conspicuous of the magazines available to me; I saw cover stories devoted to Ted Turner, "Vacation Fever," and breast cancer. Beneath these I found copies of other publications—*Newsweek, Sports Illustrated, Highlights, Reader's Digest*—all read and reread in this room's revolving door of tragedy until their covers had come loose from their staples. Most appealing were the copies of the film magazine *Cel*. This was, after all, a Hollywood hospital.

I lit a cigarette, glanced at the clock on the wall, and turned to the glossy pages of *Cel*. *Sell* would have been more like it; the magazine was almost wall-to-wall advertisements, with on-set reports about films that did not yet exist, various charts listing the weekend earnings of new releases, produced for tens of millions of dollars and then subjected to thoughtless, instant appraisals of the thumbs-up-thumbs-down variety. The most intriguing portion of the magazine, as far as I was concerned, was its classified section, where I found a number of curious listings. There was this one, filed under Research:

THROAT SPROCKETS: *Any info desperately needed and greatly appreciated for* Cel *article-in-progress. Hard cash for hard facts. Contact* Cel *PO Box* 100.

And this, under Personals:

SWM GLOVER (36 *and healthy) seeks* WF CHOKER (18–25 *and healthy) interested in reenacting* TS *scenes* 95–101. *Actual penetration only; no mimes, please. Send name and photo with return address to* Cel *PO Box* 77357.

And this, under Merchandise:

OUR NECKLACE IS "THE END"! *Exclusive facsimile* TS *choker, comfortable indigo strap with authentic fleshtone bead design. You'll swear it's the real McCoy! Only* $29.95 *(one per customer) to* CEL PO *Box* 32578.

Perhaps ten minutes later I had exhausted that issue of *Cel* and turned to the next. Flipping through the November issue I was astounded to find two stills from *Throat Sprockets*. The images did not falter, did not slip through my fingers into some other reality: they *held*. The caption read: "Mosaics for the Mouth: *Throat Sprockets* (1986)." The grain of the photos suggested frame enlargements, hardly surprising considering that no proper stills from the film were ever circulated—something I didn't know at that time, but know now. The shots appeared in the midst of an interview with somebody named Jorge Corazón Pálido, whose name was new to me.

My temperature skyrocketed with my hopes: Had I finally found the signature missing from the film? *Who did this to me? Who is the artist? Who is the artist who did this to me?*

My eagerness to read, to know, to understand, suddenly overrode my eagerness to see, as if my interest in reading had never died, but lain dormant for many years. I couldn't drink the words quickly or deeply enough, rediscovering the value of their forgotten formula. I backstepped two or three pages to the beginning of the article.

IN THE SHADOW OF EL SOMBRE
Jorge Corazón Pálido interviewed by—

Impatiently, my eyes jumped past the byline to the introductory paragraphs—

A promising UCLA film student, age 18, jumps to her death from a movie billboard high above Sunset Boulevard. A Milwaukee man, 33, calls his wife by another woman's name, attacks her without provocation, then leaves her and their two children . . . only to be arrested three weeks later in Detroit for the carnivorous slaying of a woman of the same name.

What do these seemingly disconnected lives (and deaths) have in common? According to the survivors of these bizarre scenarios the answer is an obscure fetish film called *Throat Sprockets*.

Filmed on the cheap under covert conditions in the mid-1980s, *Throat Sprockets* was acquired for U.S. release by Lotus Films, a fly-by-night distributor that promptly went out of business—apparently before any papers could be drafted declaring the company's legitimacy as a business. Strangely, the film's distribution outlets in Great Britain, France, Italy, Spain, and Japan have since vanished under similar circumstances. Because *Throat Sprockets* was issued without a credits sequence, the name of its true auteur—a man with much to explain—remains unknown.

Enter Jorge Corazón Pálido, a Catalan film journalist who professes to know the secrets behind the *Throat Sprockets* mystery. The sole respondent to our recent classified request for information about this enigmatic production, Pálido consented to be interviewed with two provisos: that his current whereabouts would not be described or reported, and that his story would be published in unedited form. "Splices are dangerous and manipulative things," he explained. I met with him at a small tavern not far from his home, and after ordering two Turkish coffees he mentioned that he had prepared an opening statement. . . .

Q: *I understand that you have an opening statement you'd like to make, Jorge?*

A: Yes. I've never spoken of these matters in print, but I've already spoken of them to too many people. My desperation to unburden myself has had both long- and short-term effects on us all. What I am about to say—all of which is true—has stained some, has made some wealthy, and has led to the disappearance of others. In essence it has used us. That's all I wanted to say. Explaining this, before I tell you what you want to know, is like crossing oneself before one blasphemes, no?

Q: *Fair enough. Let's start at the beginning: Under what circumstances did you first meet the director of* Throat Sprockets?

A: I was a student, greatly intrigued by his first feature film, *El Sombrero Grasiento* (*The Oily Hat*, 1969), which I saw during its premiere presentation at the University of Barcelona. Like most of his later films *El Sombrero Grasiento* has since been withdrawn from circulation by the director himself, and his office—if you can find it—perpetuates the legend that no print survives.

Q: *You sound skeptical. What do you remember about the picture?*

A: Even then the director was toying with (what he once described to me as) "the emotion of emulsion." *El Sombrero* contained a number of mix-matched stocks, some of which the viewer was led to trust more than others, and each print—only two were struck, as far as I know—each print was individually spliced to give audiences the impression that they were watching material so volatile that it had been heavily censored. This technique intensified the eagerness of the eye to absorb the material that did "get through" between the splices; it accelerated the brain's absorption, its processing of images.

Anyway, as the lights came up in the auditorium, I felt stunned and transformed by what I had just seen. And the auditorium had fallen completely silent. I looked around and saw that the theater was full of faces shining with the magic of changed lives.

Q: *So the film "marked" you, as critics say. What was the significance of the film's peculiar title?*

A: The title is an image, a tactile image. Spoken explanations are a poor substitute for a filmic experience; it's like trying to explain the punch line of a joke. I had to know more about this film, so I went immediately to Enrique María Calderón, the president of the film society, with whom I was well acquainted. I asked him for permission to return the sixteen-millimeter print of *El Sombrero Grasiento* to its supplier. Enrique was too busy dealing with his own heavy reaction to the picture to even think of objecting. The address on the film cans was in Barceloneta. I took the print home with me and spent the night writing about it.

   The next morning I took the public transit up to Barceloneta; this was long before . . . the movie you are researching enabled the filmmaker to relocate to a more upscale office in the heart of Las Ramblas. I climbed the stairs to the third floor of a rather narrow building and found myself standing in a downscale, disorganized office with orange shag carpeting.

   The director's assistant at that time was a Swedish woman by the name of Svea Hellstrom. I told her that I had been asked by Señor Calderón to return this print of *El Sombrero* to its director. And to no one but him. She told me that El Sombre—this was her nickname for her boss, a slurring of *"sombra"* (shadow) and *"hombre"* (man)—that El Sombre was out, and that she did not know when he might return. I was prepared for this, however, and placed on her desk along with the film cans my essay about *El Sombrero*—which had kept me up all night—which I told her had been accepted by the prestigious literary journal *El Duende*. This was a lie, of course, but it did not remain so for long. When I took my essay to the offices of *El Duende*, they accepted it without hesitation.

Q: *So your essay was published?*

A: It was published but, like the film, all copies seem to have disappeared—except one. To maintain its security I can tell you no more. Anyway, a postcard appeared one day in my mail slot. *"Usted es la única persona que entiende* El Sombrero Grasiento. *Sadilsa."* To translate, "You are the only one who understands *The Oily Hat."* He signed the note "Sadilsa," which, of course, was no more his real name than El Sombre. But it was the only name he ever gave his intimates . . . if a man so monstrous could be said to have intimates.

Q: *He wasn't even Spanish, isn't that right?*

A: Sadilsa was in fact an American expatriate, making his films and scattering them around like . . . like Johnny Bloodsucker-seed, no?

Q: *What did Sadilsa mean by that message? Didn't he feel that the film was understood by mainstream critics?*

A: It was an art film, never a popular success—nor, as my essay suggested, was it intended to be. After an unannounced screening at the festival of Sitges in 1970, Sadilsa abruptly withdrew *El Sombrero Grasiento* from distribution, which had the unexpected side-effect that my essay was elevated to a position of surrogate. Reading my essay was the only way anyone could "see" the film, in a sense. But eventually, as I've said, my essay also vanished. Some people have said that Sadilsa hired some young toughs to destroy the bulk of the print run before the issue was properly distributed, and I have also heard that he bought up the copies himself. Both scenarios seem absolutely plausible; both scenarios are also just the sort of bullshit Sadilsa delighted in concocting. It was as if the films themselves were never the end result he sought. It was as if his real goal had been to make something he could then replace with propaganda. . . .

At this point—much in the style of my initial encounter with *Throat Sprockets*—the *Cel* article ended abruptly with a postponement of truth: CONTINUED NEXT ISSUE.

The other issue of *Cel* in my waiting area was not the subsequent December issue. I bit my lip: abyss. But now I was in possession of a name or, at least, the shadow of a name to accuse. The world I walked was no longer entirely my creation and, more importantly, was not merely my perception.

I decided to search the magazine assortments in the other waiting areas for the December *Cel*. "Don't go too far," one of the nurses advised, as I darted past her station.

"A bit late for that," I told her, moving on.

There were no copies of *Cel* whatsoever in the second waiting area I visited—which, to judge from its reading material, was reserved for children, fishermen, and the clergy—but I found what I was looking for in the third waiting room. This area, like the entire floor apart from its few staff members, was vacant—or was I simply too obsessed to see anything but the words that might bring me closer to an understanding of what had happened to me and how?

BLAH BLAH SHADOW BLAH BLEL SOMBRE (Blart 2)
Jorge Corazón Pálido interviewed by Blah B. Blah
In our blah issue, we blah blah blah blah blah blah blah blah blah blah blah—

Q: *Now we know how you came to Sadilsa's attention. Can you describe your ensuing relationship with him?*

A: It was not an immediate relationship. In fact, after the loss of *El Sombrero Grasiento*, I read and heard nothing of Sadilsa or his projects for two years. This made a rather difficult personal period—I left home under unpleasant circumstances—even more strenuous for me. Movies had always been my life, but without Sadilsa something deep inside me changed and now the bulk of cinema meant nothing to me. This kind of thing happens to film enthusiasts more often than is commonly discussed. I know this is a roundabout way of answering your question. . . .

Q: *That's all right; go ahead.*

A: I mean, this deviation from cinema. Look at Truffaut. At the time of *La Nuit Américain (Day for Night,* 1974), Truffaut found he had divested himself of all his illusions about the cinema and took a long, hard look under its skirts to the plain mechanisms underneath. The result was a single perfect exclamation of love, but the films he made after that are almost the work of another man, no longer the truant child drinking milk from stolen bottles, but someone darker, more cynical and death obsessed.

A similar depletion seemed to occur in me after seeing Sadilsa's film. It was not that Sadilsa was necessarily a great filmmaker; he was *my* filmmaker, he revolutionized my thinking. He spoke for me, and I responded by speaking for him. At the same time, of course, I was responding to things in Sadilsa's work that seemed to express feelings that were already present but unarticulated within myself. In hindsight I consider him a kind of vampire . . . who drained from me the need to make my own, equally imperative, artistic expressions. The depletion made me sad.

My melancholy led me to an interest in jazz. I attended an outdoor festival on a nice, overcast day—very rare in Barcelona—and during an Astrid Gilberto performance, a storm broke. I ran for shelter, and who should I find sharing an umbrella and smoking cigarillos in the bleachers but Svea and El Sombre! The three of us found a sheltered area of the arena and talked. I was so happy to see them again. I told them about some work I'd done on the latest film by Victor Erice, whom they seemed to respect, and was told that they had just returned to Barcelona with a new film. They wouldn't say precisely where they had been filming. It is likely that they had worked without official permits. El Sombre's official residence was Liechtenstein, which made it impossible for anyone to sue him.

Q: *Was this "new film"* Throat Sprockets?

A: No. It was something called *Longue Vérification Finale avant de Lancer un Projectile dans l'Espace,* made in 1971. The French title—which literally translates as "Extended, Last-Minute Verification Before the Launching of a Missile into Space" or, more concisely in English, "Countdown"—indicated to me that they had been filming somewhere in France. The significance of the title lies in the fact that the film was presented as a series of "dailies"; that is, a nonlinear collection of scenes and alternate takes from an as-yet-unedited motion picture, separated by countdowns of film leader. Sadilsa stood there like a cigar-store Indian, but Svea told me, "El Sombre is very eager to hear your reaction to what he has filmed." She immediately invited me to a private screening of the film the next day.

As you can imagine, I was so excited, I could barely sleep. I kept thinking that my life was finally going to get back on track. The next day finally came; Svea flagged me down outside the building and escorted me into the screening room, where Sadilsa was seated in the rear. He nodded his hello. And the movie! Once again I felt completely rejuvenated by the experience! Afterward my head felt as if all of its windows had been opened to invite a wonderful housecleaning breeze. Both of my hosts disappeared sometime during the screening. And so I wrote a long and appreciative letter, for Sadilsa's eyes only.

I praised his highly original concept of using raw dailies and alternate takes of the same scenes to tell and lend shading to his obsessive story; the hypnotic, accumulative effect of the interjections of countdown leader (6, 5, 4, 3, blip!); and, also, the unexpected impact of the gunshot fired into the camera at the very end of the film, which permitted the full French title to bloom into an especially satisfying, resoundingly bitter double entendre. The bullet being—

Q: *Yes, the missile launched into space. It sounds pretty intriguing.*

A: Yes, but you see, I hadn't been made to understand prior to the screening that I was being invited to see *only their dailies*—not the completed picture! Svea confided in me a couple of weeks before her suicide that this was indeed the case; that Sadilsa himself had originally every intention of editing the film together in the traditional fashion but, after receiving my written accolades, decided to "lock it down" the way it was.

Q: *How did he respond to your letter?*

A: To respond to my letter would be an admission that he'd seen it, read it, and been influenced by it, no? You might say that the film itself was his answer to my letter— which, incidentally, was conveniently misplaced in Svea's filing hell. Sadilsa then "rewarded" my observations by inviting me to observe his working techniques at first hand, in the role of his assistant and script supervisor. As the saying goes, Keep your friends close, but keep your enemies closer.

Q: *But wasn't "script supervisor" Svea Hellstrom's job definition?*

A: No, Svea was essentially in charge of his office and, when he was filming, served as a guerrilla-style production manager.

Q: *I would imagine from your job description that you worked long hours, and were in a position to observe a variety of Sadilsa's moods.*

A: Absolutely, but there was a wall of privacy that I continually bumped against in nearly all my dealings with El Sombre. He liked his pretensions. I remember he once showed to me a scene that had not yet been given sound. The cutting was very fluid, patient, even musical—so I asked him afterward if the score had already been written. He looked at me with some amazement and said, "Idiot, the film always comes before the music—never the other way around." To which I said, "All art aspires to the condition of music." I'll never forget the look he gave me.

Q: *And what about on a more personal level?*

A: Well, you know how it is when you meet anyone with whom you share a large number of interests, personal or professional. You exchange information, share experiences and funny stories, eventually extend your relationship by opening yourselves mutually to stories of misfortune or heartbreak—in short, you become like friends, no? It was strange with Sadilsa. He knew so much about the cinema, yet he had no passion for it. I never knew him to attend a film other than those he made, and he would never say how he had become interested or name the films that had influenced or stimulated his thinking.

Despite this Sadilsa knew so many things that I felt I needed to know. He maintained an approachable but inevitably aloof attitude toward me, the kind of attitude that inspires a person of unequal standing—as I understood myself to be—to attempt to gain equality through the sharing of confidences, secrets. The more terrible the secrets, the greater the confidence, no?

As I look back on the few years I spent with him, Sadilsa learned a lot about me, things I wish I could recover from him—incriminating secrets of the heart, and so forth—and I learned also many things about him, more through observation than admission—but, after all that time, I must admit I know absolutely nothing *of* him. His breast never opened to me.

Q: *What about his wallet? What did he pay you for working as his— what did you say—his script supervisor and assistant?*

A: I thought of myself as an apprentice; I worked for nothing. I worked for the sake of my own education, for experience.

Q: *Would you say this was a mistake?*

A: In any other business, no. But the film business, especially today, values only that which has a dollar (or power) value attached; the two are absolutely synonymous. If you work in the film business for nothing, you, too, are nothing; furthermore, you will never be hired, because you have already established that you will work for nothing. It was a mistake, yes. I should have done as my university friends did—rent, borrow, or steal a thirty-five-millimeter camera and power-pack, splice together unexposed film ends from garbage cans for film stock, and slap something together that pretends to have a message. Costa-Gavras, Junior! But remember, I was not passionate in my thinking; I was disillusioned with the cinema. My obsession was not with films, but with *Sadilsa's* films. My fascination was so powerful that all my other interests were eclipsed.

Even my own personal ambitions for a career were eclipsed. The demands of my apprenticeship forced me to drop out of my last year at university. A love of film must be polygamous to be healthy; my obsession with Sadilsa's work was like a perverse monogamy. I understood this even at the time, but I had to follow my fascination through to its end. How else was I to accomplish this? My path was plain.

Q: *Do you think your devotion to Sadilsa was a mistake?*

A: "Mistake" implies a *choice*, you see. . . .

Q: *You proved your abilities, yet no one was willing to pay you what they were worth? Why do you think the film business is set up this way?*

A: It keeps out the kinds of creative, independent, free-thinking people who truly love the cinema, who would—given the opportunity—make important and truthful and mature films, and might restore magic to our poor, deceased cinema and dignity to its juvenilized audience—in other words, exactly the kinds of people who would not hesitate to spit on its executors' filthy game. Sadilsa used to look at my screenplays, the ones that I wrote to console myself in the evenings, and he would tell me that they were too sophisticated. I couldn't understand the difference between his sophistication and my own, what made his sophistication produceable and mine impossible.

Q: *With no money, how did you live?*

A: I lived on friendly charity, eating always less than my fill of friends' food, sleeping on their couches and walking their dogs and listening to their bedtime sounds and, afterward, listening to their wives ask when the guest room would be a living room again. When I got kicked out, I sold blood until I found another living room to turn into a guest room. There were days when I was actually told that my blood was no good, that I was undernourished. And there were nights when I cried a little, for not having even enough money to take a woman of my own out to dinner, or because I realized that I no longer said hello anymore to the women I saw and might like to know. I couldn't. What could I possibly offer them?

Q: *How did things start to turn around?*

A: Hunger is not good for children, but it can make an adult very observant. When Sadilsa wasn't making a film (which was obviously most of the time), and there was no craft service table to feed me, I went through periods in which I was essentially starving. My anger about the structure of the film business was a kind of naïveté, and it had blinded me. The truth is, films are not works of art. You can tell a lover of films that there is no art in the cinema and he will never believe you; the idea is so alien that he cannot even hear it! Films allow other things to become possible. The industry starves its artists—first, to discourage them, but also to keep them so preoccupied with their stomachs that they cannot see *beyond* the money structure of the film business.

Believe me, the money part is only the hardened surface—the crust, if you will. You, as a reporter of the cinema, must be brave and look under it. You must see the maggots, their industry. The money is nothing at all. The money, the weekend box-office figures, the millions that the big stars make, all this you can read about in any newspaper or see reported on any television program. The monetary facts are now so well publicized that they have become meaningless.

At the same moment I promised myself that I would not

allow the cinema I once loved to destroy me, I had a terrible, hallucinatory vision of the truth behind the film industry. I suddenly saw through the coined spires of its money structure—to the bacchanalia of its *power* structure.

The second portion of the Pálido interview ended here, just as abruptly as the first, with the promise of a conclusion in the January *Cel*, which was nowhere to be found. In fact, as I later learned, *Cel* had ceased to exist with its December issue. Someone somewhere had seen to it that Jorge Corazón Pálido's final revelations would never see the light of day.

The depression that came with that knowledge was reserved for later; at that moment I felt only dejection. I felt tugged by a kind of obligation to return to the waiting area assigned to me, but I found something very seductive about that last waiting area on the hospital's other side, positioned at the end of the hall around the closest corner from the room where I had been told to wait. Its furniture was made of the same vanilla vinyl cushions prevailing everywhere else—chosen, no doubt, by a staff psychologist who found those creamy surfaces pleasingly neutral—but their comfort was eclipsed by a most welcome cigarette machine, the only one on the entire floor. I leaned against it, as if it were a reassuring friend, a jukebox stocked with reassuring records, and read the selections displayed in tiny frames beneath its glass façade. Only one choice was represented: CONSOLIDATIONS, CONSOLIDATIONS, CONSOLIDATIONS. . . .

My vision was frazzled; I hadn't slept in nearly thirty hours. I shoved my money into the machine, yanked its pinball handle, and watched as it thudded back on its coil, tripping a pack of my brand down its chute. I held the pack to my nose and took a deep whiff of its packaged tobaccos; my head and vision cleared. CONSOLATIONS, CONSOLATIONS, CONSOLATIONS . . .

I stripped the cellophane collar from the pack and hungrily smoked my Consolation while continuing on an evasive circuit of the corridors. A few steps away from the cigarette machine I passed a small open room and, thinking that I might find Emma recovering inside, doubled back to investigate. There, for the space of a portal, the hospital's dominant whiteness was welcomely interrupted with recessed splashes of vivid red and indigo. I dropped my cigarette and passed through a yawn of white pleated draperies into the heightened environment of a small auditorium defined by six richly lacquered cedar pews, an illuminated cyclorama of the crucifixion in stained glass, and a central podium emblazoned with the symbol of that crucifixion in gold leaf.

I had found the hospital chapel.

I took a seat in that otherwise empty sanctuary, and had the distinct impression of stepping outside my predicament, of finding a place where I might view my life with the necessary objectivity to make future plans. I reflected on Emma's dream and its corrosive effect on the dreams she and I had already realized—the time I descended on her, when she turned on me and said, her gaze looking past me to virgin vistas, "No—that's weak tea."

After several minutes of my replaying that sobering pronouncement in my mind, a priest appeared. Shuffling down the aisle, he performed a half-kneel of genuflection and mounted the stage. He busied himself there with flower baskets for some moments, before noticing me.

"I'm sorry, I didn't see you out there," he said. "A bit early, aren't we?"

I told him that I didn't understand.

"The memorial service won't be for another hour, hour and a half."

"Oh," I said, "I'm not here for that."

"You here for confession? Or simple privacy?"

"I don't know," I confessed. "I feel more comfortable here, somehow, than I did out there. Everything out there is so white, it's blinding."

"Blindness sometimes helps us to look inside," he said, setting down the flower baskets and ruffling his thick graying hair. He sent a piercing stare through his dark-rimmed glasses into the shadows where I sat and, as if finding himself suddenly intrigued by this delirious stranger, joined me in my pew. He didn't bother to shake my hand or to identify himself; he cut to the chase. "A loved one of yours," he assumed, "is a patient here?"

It was so refreshing to see someone whose collar implied an innocence that I felt an eagerness to appease him. "Yes," I said.

"Parent or spouse?"

"Spouse," I supposed, "but not in the eyes of God, as they say."

"I see. What's her condition?"

"They tell me she's stable, but . . . The condition of our relationship is another story."

"Tell it."

"Tell me," I asked after a gravid pause, "how is it possible to live with someone for a year—to give entirely of yourself to them—to share everything with them, even the most—unspeakable things and then, suddenly, when they need you the most—it's as if you're no longer certain of who they are, or if you've ever really known them at all?"

"It's possible because it happens with everyone, every day, across the board," he answered promptly, as if he had answered this question before, even every day. "The man I am in this small chapel—that's not the me who can't help smoking smelly cigars after eating blue cheese, or the me who enjoys reading Ken Follett. We're all complex individuals even as we stand alone, and human company should be considered a blessing, for the ways it allows us to further complicate—to *evolve*, if you will—the gift of our selves."

"If I don't know the woman I supposedly love, how can I be sure that I even know myself?"

"That's a serious question, but take comfort in the fact that it isn't really for us to know anyone, even ourselves, completely.

That is for a higher sensibility, you might say. We all need to know that there's a space within ourselves that can't be reached from outside, that can't be reached *physically*. That's what gives us the initiative to look inside, to reserve a portion of ourselves for contemplative living. That's what shows us the way to God. That's why we keep it so dark in here."

"I've been trying to reach that plane—physically," I said.

"Your wires are crossed," the priest insisted. "It can't be done. The only experience that approaches that level of communion, so far as I know, is the ceremony of the Blessed Sacrament. But something tells me you're not a Catholic."

"No," I hedged, "but this—woman and I, we've—we've been practicing a form of—*secular* communion."

The priest stilled. He remained quiet for so long that I feared he hadn't heard me, that I would have to repeat myself, perhaps even rephrase myself with greater candor or, failing that, outright obscenity. Then, tremulously and with great solemnity, he crossed himself. His mouth went through the motions of mumbling, his words unspoken as he sought their most diplomatic focus.

"The tragedy here," he stammered, "is that you are not the first to seek transcendence in such a perversion, and you will not be the last."

Perversion. The word, its alien taint, came like a slap. It must have shown.

"Oh, don't misunderstand me," he said quickly, responding to my wince. "I'm using the term advisedly," he explained, "in its medical appliance, not judgmentally. I understand perversion. I've seen my firsthand share. The facts of these matters don't really concern me. What does concern me, however, are the implications of this societal symptom."

"I don't follow you."

"You're what—late twenties?"

"Early thirties."

He smiled cryptically. "Well, there you go. That's Danger Time, isn't it? That's the time of life when healthy young men find themselves going astray, standing alone in a dark wood, as the poet said. They enter into affairs, supposing that by—that by taking a bite out of life, shall we say, that they might somehow beat the odds and live forever. That by husbanding a woman not their wife in the eyes of God, that they might thereby escape notice on the day of judgment. A lot of men come back to the church in their early thirties. Really, you'd be surprised. You know, I have a kind of theory about all this . . . business," he added, gesturing with two fingers to his throat.

I couldn't believe what I was hearing, but I let him ramble on, presuming that this private sermon would eventually circle back to Emma and me and leave me wiser.

"It's crossed my mind," the priest continued, "while reading about the related deaths in the papers and counseling the people who wander through here on occasion, that this sort of thing is perhaps to be expected in human behavior. We are animals born in blood, and therefore, we somehow feel that we must be restored to blood. It's not unlike the ways in which men seek, in their sexual experience, a symbolic return to the womb or to the testes. This is natural behavior, but counterproductive to society. This is the reason we've always had war. It is a kind of global catharsis. War channels our aggressive animal energies against convenient foes, negative against negative to form a positive. There's always a perversion of society before a war. War is declared to consolidate societies that might otherwise consume themselves.

"Now, *your* generation," he said with potent specificity, "is the first in the history of this young country that hasn't known war. And so it's reacting in the only way it can," he explained, again jabbing at his collared throat with forked fingers, "having been deprived of its ritual return to the blood."

"Maybe you don't get to see much TV in your line of work," I said, "but aren't you forgetting the Gulf War?"

"The Gulf War," spat the priest. "You're young—you wouldn't know a real war—forgive me this—if it came up and bit you. Believe me, that was no war. Real war convulses a country, all countries, even the countries of the clouds. Real war isn't a tiny conflict you have to watch under a microscope called television. A war is a national wound that lies open for years—not a *week* of raids followed by a *year* of parades. Your generation doesn't know any better. But, evidently, your bodies *do.*"

"Of course it was a war," I protested. "There were casualties."

"Peacetime has casualties," mocked the priest. "Mark my words: This government we've elected will learn soon enough that this 'war' didn't have the desired effect."

"Namely?"

"The reassignment of perverse energy, as I've said. Young America isn't yet nauseated by bloodshed. Having come out of the sixties your generation considers itself too civilized for real war. And without that catharsis to satisfy your inherent bloodlust, you are seeking that fulfillment elsewhere—wherever you can find it, in movie theaters, in bedrooms, and blood banks. That's why it qualifies, literally, as a *perversion.* It's a natural energy, a genetic memory not yet lost, being channeled aberrantly—toward a civilized expression, in a world we've deliberately designed without outlets for its expression, thinking that might somehow weed out what's worst in us. But it hasn't. Not yet, anyway. So don't think for a moment that your life-style shocks me. I've seen worse, and I've drowned the memory in the most potent blood available to man."

I thanked the priest for his time and rose to leave. "You've given me a good deal to think about."

"Then I've done my job," he said. "What will you do now?"

I nodded toward the other side of the building. "I'd better be getting back. They may have some news, be looking for me."

"Do you think you can find your way back?"

"If it's not too late."

· · ·

I couldn't help thinking back—looking down from the observatory window, many hours later, at the unchanging scenes below of the Tinsel Town chokers hassling the dark-windowed limousines that darted along the Sunset Strip—back to the story of how so many men and women of my parents' generation had met: at a USO dance, where the deathbound looks in soldiers' eyes dissolved the unwillingness that USO girls normally felt in peacetime. The priest's theory made sense. That attraction and that danger recurred predictably, peristaltically, throughout history— to keep things happening, to keep our soil turned and tilled. Mine: the first generation of American men kept clear of war, placed hopelessly and equidistantly between our aspirations to a higher plane and our essentially animal instincts, which told us that we had survived this long only by fucking what we feared and eating what we killed.

Any dream, any nightmare, any armchair sociology, was preferable to contemplating the moment when my waiting would end, and the moment beyond that when Emma and I would be reunited—if, indeed, it did unite us.

· · ·

"Sir? Will you follow me, please?"

When a masked surgeon finally appeared and beckoned me to follow, it seemed more a presentiment than a moment of truth. Infinite hours had passed in waiting but suddenly, with the arrival of my guide, I felt the need to hold back from the inevitable for a while longer, aggravated by the urgency expressed by a doctor whose valuable time was being wasted.

"Is she all right?" I asked, but he remained silent, frozen in his beckoning attitude at the side of the DO NOT ENTER doors. I followed him through the forbidding doors, running several paces behind, and felt myself pulled inexorably, on the strength of his personal magnetism alone, toward some unrequited shock or ultimate reality that demanded a witness to achieve its full definition. The tenebrous passages between us and our vague destination were themselves defined only by the scent of clinical antiseptics and door numbers hovering in stark luminosity. I caught glimpses through patients' doors left open a crack, glimpses of private agonies and nudities, and I had no idea of where I was being led, entrusting my guidance entirely to the floating whiteness of the doctor's spotless surgical apron.

"Where are you taking me?" I asked.

His white rubber glove emerged from the darkness, wriggling two elastic fingers in an invitation to come on, come on. "Where you want to go," the doctor teased, voice muffled through his surgical mask.

"All these doors . . ."

"Options," the surgeon exclaimed. "They all lead somewhere!"

"But we're bypassing them all," I fretted.

The surgeon laughed: " 'Bypass!' Isn't that *marvelous!*"

The joke I didn't understand somehow put us on an even keel; the surgeon draped his white arm over my shoulder for a while as we hustled past another series of doors, then he released me and allowed himself to fall behind. The skintight gloves prodding periodically at my back suggested that I wasn't moving fast enough to suit him—but where *was* I going? I looked over my shoulder, hoping to gain a clue from his eyes, but behind me and the rudder of those goading gloves, I saw nothing but a darkness that trailed behind me for miles, years—I couldn't have possibly found my way back to where we started.

I was taken past the recovery rooms and shown into a tiled area with a long, fauceted trough. Doctors and nurses in surgical garb stood around, awaiting my arrival, and drew up their surgical masks before I could score a proper look at their faces. As one of them readied his hands for surgery with sterilizing Brylcreem and talc, a flame-haired nurse in catty glasses shoved the accoutrements of a carryout lunch into my arms.

"Where is Dr. Allcome?" I asked.

"Dr. Allcome—there *is* no Dr. Allcome," the nurse told me. "That's a name that hospitals use on their public address systems when they need all available hands to assist in an emergency. It prevents the patients and visitors from becoming alarmed."

"Is this an emergency?"

"You tell us!" the nurse groused.

"This can't be happening," I informed her. "How do I get out of here?"

"That depends entirely on where you want to go."

"Back," I said. "I have to get back."

I butted through another pair of swinging doors, through which I emerged into an operating theater the size of a small church. Candlelight caressed the sterling edges of surgical silver and the cloth-masked faces of male and female attendants like the brush of Rembrandt. Enveloping the operating table itself in the center of the room was an elaborate tableau of tented sheets, upended bottles of colorless nutriments weeping into dark venereal tubes, and a breathing concertina cautiously minded by an anesthetist. The sheets covering the operating table were green, the queasy green that sky blue becomes on film when it hasn't been timed right, or when film stock is allowed to cook in its can, unloaded for weeks on some hellishly hot location in New Guinea or South Africa; they billowed in the breeze of a broken backstage window. I was guided toward this unseemly altar like the bridegroom at a midnight ceremony in the heart of a forest. I followed the sound of outbreaking applause above my head to a gathering of almost everyone I had ever known and loved, seated in the pentagonal bleachers of its crystal steeple.

Everything up to now, I seemed to hear from an adjoining theater, *had been a preparation for this moment. Everything up to now had given him an opportunity in which to slowly summon the courage required for the test that, at last, had come.*

The sound of familiar breathing from the operating table attracted me to its edge. Framed within the sheeting was the perfect oval of my love's face, like a mask floating along the surface of a verdant pond; she turned her conscious eyes on me. With a beatific smile that made her radiant, her mouth whispered, "Happy Anniversary."

Below her face the sheeting lay in two diagonal folds like a pair of wings at rest. A surgeon's classical hand intruded delicately into her locus of light to individually peel back these twin layers, exposing a perfectly tailored aperture in the linen that bared her chest from clavicle to abdomen. Already in place was a completed surgical inscription: two scarlet trenches intersecting between her golden breasts that gleamed wetly to the rhythm of her breathing: an X.

Lying on that perverse bier of seduction Emma exuded an extraordinary, touching vulnerability. She wanted her dream realized to the extent of arranging it, as an anniversary gift to us, in front of God and the whole world. She did not hesitate for one moment to articulate her former yearnings, so near the moment of their realization, with the same words used when this moment had seemed unattainable.

"I've never known such love," she said. "I want to, though . . . I want to, though. . . ."

He was loved without bounds. Did he have the courage to return this gift of boundless love?

Only the suspicion that the moment wasn't quite real encouraged me to proceed. At the warming invitation of her eyes I reached out and placed my hands, almost testingly, on her breasts. Cold and almost wooden to the touch, I tried to rub some life into them. The effect of this friction was unexpected: everything else in or above the operating theater—its equipment, our witnesses—became excluded from my senses, which perceived no light but that which was emitted by her face and her breasts, luminous islands in impossible darkness. The more I tried rubbing warmth back into her, the more the panels of her chest seemed to thrust forward, widening her incision and forcing it open. There was no bleeding—only a rapturous broadening of light from behind those golden cupboard doors, the aurora of the beating heart within.

I beheld her heart, overwhelmed by its incandescence, touched by the trust implicit in its easily bruised contours; I took it in my hands and was destroyed, reinvented—its trust repaid.

Disbelieving, I looked up from this Ultimate Gift and saw Paige smiling down on me with all the wisdom, kindness, and heavenly grace of a Madonna. Her incisions were now healed, her breasts were warm, and we were home again.

Damnation was showing me the sum of my losses.

5

Everything that begins in mystery, ends in practical politics.

Charles Péguy

THE PALACE OF WISDOM

YOU HAVEN'T UNDERSTOOD A WORD I'VE SAID.

I found this place on the far end of the long bridge that leads to old age, guided here by the kindness of others; I have often despaired of ever finding this place, fearing that these people have only been describing a course away from themselves. So with Christian charity let us pretend that all the directions I was given were deliberate—from Friendship to Chicago to Washington, D.C., to Los Angeles to Amsterdam to Barcelona to here—and that this war-zone rubble is in fact the ruins of the Palace of Wisdom.

I have had few companions on my journey to this moment, and none at all for some time. The throats of women my own age have little appeal for me; as the skin advances through the years, it loses its moisture, smoothness, and firmity, leaving the necks of men and women alike with only a weathered and withered exaggeration of their former sensuality. The people I have told you about, in brief and in detail, have long since vanished from the blur of my life and gone into a past more readable than my present has ever been, and I can describe them as well as I have only because my yearning for them all is so acute.

I yearn for Emma, whose obsessions proved to be transitory while mine were in permanent stasis; I yearn for the Old Man, who apologized for having to fire me when the company's reputation could no longer endure the scandal of keeping me aboard; I yearn for Myla Monteith, Kirsten Fosseck, Colleen Sangster, and all the other women who grazed my life before passing into the dense brushstrokes of life's mystery; I yearn for my country, where a failed educational system has undermined the reliability of majority rule and made elections a dangerous farce, where people persist in looking for easy answers in a gridlock of gunmetal and bureaucracy; and, like those who look to simpler times for solutions to their problems, I yearn most deeply for Paige. In the course of a life I have largely ignored and scarcely have a right to call my own, I've lost them all, and I've journeyed here to learn why.

• • •

You haven't understood a word of this, but I might as well prattle on; I, like the people I've told you about, will soon be gone. My erasure has already begun here, in the ruins of this hilltop *cinemateca.*

It was during my years in Amsterdam that I first heard rumor of a secret and privately owned archive, somewhere on the continent, that held every document, every article, every photograph and poster, every piece of memorabilia, every shred of truth pertaining to the phenomenon known as *Throat Sprockets.* To walk across its bombed marble floors, strangely dignified in their decomposure, is to traverse the shaved head of a conquered art— odd pages from film periodicals lay burned and scattered or blown by the four winds beyond retrieval . . . the subterranean photo files have been ventilated by machine-gun fire . . . the few remaining reels of film that the assailants and saviors of this place have left behind have been welded by oppressive, roofless sunlight to their plastic yellow cores. It was impossible, seeing such wanton destruction after coming so far, to do anything but collapse on these crumbling stone stairs and cry heavily into my own two hands.

I wasn't aware that you were watching me from inside, gauging the intentions of this *loco americano*. My tears made me appear safe; they must have seemed familiar to you. Your small hand touched my shoulder and I opened my eyes—first on those stubby little fingers with bitten nails, then on the small, dirty, sun-browned face of an uncomprehending child, brunette and sullen, somehow surviving these uncertain times in these ruins, a target already stricken. You couldn't be more than six years old. Your dress was filthy and torn in a dozen places, and perhaps half a size too small. You were hugging to yourself some things you had found scattered about the area. I wondered if your dress had also been a found object, or if the stress of your growing body against the fabric was an indication of how long you had been living as an orphan of the desert.

To help me forget my tears you dumped your scraps in my lap —things your little hands had rescued from the rubble of the collapsed upper floors on the northeastern side, or collected from the blackened brush lining the hillside that rises to this small plateau—things that you had found long before my arrival, found pretty, and preserved. I examined your findings as you watched. There were particolored wardrobe sketches for forgotten musicals, an old laminated program book for *This Is Cinerama*, and a single ballet slipper with a numbered MGM production label stitched into its heel—the flotsam of old Hollywood. My personal obsession with *Throat Sprockets* was such that it hadn't occurred to me that this fabled *cinemateca* might also house other collections. I felt nauseated at the prospect that perhaps nothing had survived of the *Throat Sprockets* archives. Had everything been destroyed by the guns of the resistance? If so, had the collection been catalogued? Had the catalogue survived? Even a laundry list of items might be enlightening. . . .

During all of my questions your eyes stared back at me: feral, black, shaken. You didn't understand a word I said.

Relieving me of my cane, you took my hand and led me through the still-standing portal of this fallen *fachada*, walking ahead once we were inside to alert me to sensitive passages, hidden chasms in the floor, walls too weak for even an old man to lean against. We walked over fragments of brick and stone that had rained down upon a stratum of scorched and scattered eight-by-ten photos, the familiar eyes of Bela Lugosi, Joan Blackman, Pamela Franklin, and others staring up through the rubble of today from a monochromatic past. The sense of the *cinemateca*'s own past had not been blown away. Enough could be seen in the remains of the auditorium—which had once screened films for local men and women and their families—to perceive the grandeur that must once have been.

"You—see movies—here?" I asked you.

Remember what you said, *chiquita*? "Papa bring. We see Charlot."

Seeing my frown, you performed a perfect Chaplin walk with my cane, tottering around a corner on your bare heel.

I followed you around the corner into one of the central research areas. The resistance propaganda that I'd heard, boasting of the *cinemateca*'s incalculable losses, had not been overstated, but an encouraging amount of material appeared to be intact, oblivious of or merely unsettled by the violence. Even so, there was little to be celebrated in this small margin of grace; it only meant that the so-called Armies of God were not yet through with this place. They would be coming back.

We had to work fast. "*Throat Sprockets*," I told you, with little hope that you would understand me. "I need anything, anything at all to do with *Throat Sprockets*." Then I remembered the sign language of the priest and pointed two fingers at the side of my neck. You disappeared into the bowels of these ruins.

In the sunlight left to the *cinemateca*'s gigantic southwestern wing, which had miraculously survived the raids more or less intact, I busied myself with trying to toggle a Steenbeck viewing console back to life; even if the building's electricity had not been cut, it was likely that the vibrations of attack had unsettled its works. I felt a poke at my side. You, my little companion, were jabbing me with a surprise you had found—some kind of fire-ravaged, coverless pamphlet. You seemed impatient with my pre-occupation with the film equipment.

"No look," you reprimanded me. "¡Lee!"

I uprighted an overturned chair and took a seat at the console. I opened the book—being uncovered and with no title page, it was already in a sense opened—handling it gingerly, careful not to inflict any additional stress upon it. Framed in carbon on a brown-edged leaf were the following words:

A young country girl name of Crockett
Lured beaux with her Grandmother's locket;
Its gold chain dealt a scrape
    to her delicate nape—
"If you ain't tried sprocket, don't knock it!"

I laughed with delight; you had found something! ¡Brava, chiquita! It was a volume of specialized limericks, the kind that used to be sold in dirty-book stores, a piece of trendy, rip-off merchandise. It was such a stupid thing to make an old man cry. Knowing that you might misinterpret my tears and think you had somehow hurt my feelings, I thanked you with the warmest smile I could muster.

Inquisitively, you reached for my wattles, flicked at them, and called me "Pollo." This made us both laugh more in earnest.

The next limerick that caught my eye was this:

I was sent a love note in red pen
Asking when we might sprocket again.
My character flawed,

I hemmed and I hawed—
So the note went to ten other men.

And near the end of the crumbling volume:

There once was a choker named Mary—
No virgin, so clients were wary.
So with AmEx gold-plated,
       she had reinstated
A brand-new, unbreakable cherry!

That last poem somewhat soured my pleasure at finding that arti-
fact because, in the innocuous sequence of those three limericks,
the entire arc of the *Throat Sprockets* phenomenon was encom-
passed in devilishly accurate miniature—from the carefree allure
of the first limerick, which closed by extending a copycat invitation to its reader, much as the film had done to its viewers—to
the second one's bittersweet themes of hesitancy and disillusion-
ment, which had characterized my own period of temptation and
indecision—to the monstrous caricatures of the third, indicative
of the fear and prejudice that ultimately led to the founding of
cryptofascist organizations like STOKER.

"Where did you find this?" I asked. You gave no response, so I
simplified my question as best I could: "Where? *¿Dónde?*"

You took my hand and led me away from the Steenbeck to
precisely the treasure trove I had come to find. Most of the ceiling was darkening sky, most of the items preserved below had
been exposed to recurrent sun and rain and raids, but most of the
periodicals and other paper materials were still on hand in one
piece, still legible. With so little time I had to know exactly where
to look to find anything of particular value, so I rummaged
through various files until I located something familiar, something
portentous. It happened to be a packet labeled "Pálido, Jorge
Corazón."

Unbelievably, the file contained everything I could have asked for, including the legendary "lost" issue of *El Duende*, containing Pálido's essay about *El Sombrero Grasiento* (the Spanish text was much too advanced for me to decipher), as well as the manuscript of the previously unpublished third portion of his *Cel* interview. I crammed the entire file into my shoulder bag.

And then a loud thud came from your side of the room, reverberating through the immense emptiness. I jumped, sensitive (under the circumstances) to sudden outbursts. You were standing above a large leather-bound book, which you had loudly dropped, because it was far too heavy for your little arms to carry. You knelt beside it and slapped the cover, which read, *The Complete Works of William Shakespeare*.

"¿Americano?" you asked, pointing to the name.

"Close enough," I said, as I hobbled over to you.

I also knelt, feeling more than a little awed in the presence of this important relic of movie history. I opened its covers and searched out *Antony and Cleopatra* in the table of contents, then turned to the tragedy's final page, itself a stage upon which a pivotal moment of cinematic history had been played. The black type stood out well against the dried, red blotch. I scanned the text with my failing eyes, remembering precisely how the actress had spoken those words, and ran my palm over the soiled page.

At long last, *contact.*

Time had turned the splash of human wine to a more autumnal hue. *Blood may be thicker than water*, I thought, *but it's less permanent than ink.*

Under a sky too overcast for reading, a premature nightfall, I shared with you the last of the dried fruit from my shoulder bag. Even I felt that it had not been enough, and who knows how long you had been starving out here in the elements? All at once, you startled me by folding up, quick as a switchblade, into a squatting position. Your movements were so swift and expert that I felt answered, that you had been surviving off the land on your wits alone for quite some time.

"*¿Qué* es?" I whispered, my fears of a surprise attack realerted.

Your eyes were intent on the brush beyond a collapsed wall, ravenous, large like the eyes of a nocturnal animal.

"Shhh," you hissed. "A *conejo.*"

With that explanation you rose and leapt through the aperture with accustomed litheness.

And now night has come in authenticity, and under its star-feathered wing I have told you the only story I know. I knew you wouldn't understand a word I said, and somehow this has helped me to divest myself fully of a lifetime of secrets. You didn't understand, but I thank you—*¡gracias, chiquita!*—for listening so intently to everything, without the patterns of judgment or prejudice once clouding your expression as I admitted to the least attractive aspects of my character. On the opposite side of our campfire you lay under a long, rain-warped library table upon which moss has begun to grow, watching me through flickering light with the face that has always watched me. In the course of my story the sticks fueling our campfire moldered into ash and smoke. I spied in the flames some crossed kindling in the form of a collapsing crucifix, as well as the bones of the rabbit you caught. And now my tired little companion, my huntress, my audience—sedated by the all-too-infrequent comforts of a bedtime story and a full stomach—has murmured softly, *"Bue'noches, Señor Pollo,"* and fallen asleep as a final sigh of smoke lifts from the embers.

• • •

I open *The Complete Works of William Shakespeare,* look at the famous stain inside, and think to myself, *First you were the one on the screen at the Eros. You fed my eyes.* The flickering of the fire is untrustworthy, and as I watch, the bloody page seems to become the fortuitous paint spill outside La Proscenium at Friendship Mall, somewhere on the other side of the globe. . . . *Then you were the one at the art-*

supplies store. You fed my fantasies. The tongue of paint continues to extend into the shape of the library table across the room from me, providing a roof over the sleeping head of her latest incarnation. . . . *And now I find you at this distant, bombed-out* cinemateca. *You fed my stomach.*

My Love. My Type. My Muse.

The stained page calls out to me, demanding some kind of requital, but the moment is not yet right. I close the book's covers and stash it away inside my shoulder bag, making its theft official. I throw some heavy Halliwell film guides on the fire, and as the room enjoys a resurgence of warmth and light, I turn my attention to the Pálido file and the unpublished portion of his interview.

I was ready for answers.

Q: *I don't quite understand what you mean by "the bacchanalia of its power structure," Jorge.*

A: In the film industry power is everything. I do not mean power in the sense of wealth or position, but power in the sense of *horror.* If the film industry is terrified of an individual, anything becomes possible for that person. For example: there is a certain individual—I cannot mention his name because he is very famous—who used horror as a method to gain fame and notoriety in Hollywood. He had made a few films, mostly unsuccessful, and there came a time when he was hospitalized for some minor surgery. He made a point of instructing his publicist that no explanation, apart from "minor surgery," be given to the press. Rumors had abounded of his homosexuality, so there was an immediate suspicion among the press that his hospital visit was AIDS related. Well, in time, someone on the hospital staff let slip that his surgery had been rectal. It was not long before word got around that this fellow and his boyfriend had been involved in "gerbil races"—stuffing gerbils inside each other's rectums. The boyfriend had been lucky, but in the case of this celebrity, word got around that the poor animal had died of suffocation inside his body.

Q: *That's the most disgusting thing I've ever heard.*

A: The beauty of this story is that journalists eventually confronted his publicist with the rumor. They demanded to know the true nature of his surgery, or they would go to print with the rumor. Shortly after the confrontation the publicist held a press conference and said, "It's very simple, really—he was having a *mole* removed."

When the celebrity was released from what had actually been the minor surgery described by his publicist, he found himself eminently bankable. His potentiality for darkness both fascinated and repulsed the Hollywood money men, but it also showed that he was not only capable of anything—an important trait for stardom—but that he could also keep secrets, and keep them with style.

The same techniques work for women as well. I know of one case in which a young actress, a wholesome girl typecast in TV situation comedies, faked her own death in a *faux* snuff film in order to stage her comeback. Of course, anyone who saw the film and then saw her name on an audition sheet agreed to see her. They had seen her in the worst possible situation, with nothing comic about it, and could suddenly "see" her in more serious roles. And these men who hired her were also deeply afraid of being exposed as collectors of snuff films. And today her studio is promoting her latest performance with "For Your Consideration" advertisements for the Best Actress Academy Award. . . .

Q: *What you're telling me is incredible. How did these insights help to reconnect you with Sadilsa?*

A: Years had passed without a new film from Sadilsa, and it suddenly dawned on me that he was waiting for me to supply him with an idea. I decided to exact a kind of revenge for his mistreatment of me, so I began sending him paragraphs clipped from stories I found in various newspapers and magazines. It was my expectation that he would use these materials and leave himself vulnerable to court action by the rightful authors of these stories. Instead, I was summoned one day to his office by Svea, who asked if I was available to act as an assistant on El Sombre's new film, which was to begin production shortly. I agreed, wanting desperately to see that ship go down with its cold-blooded captain.

When I met with El Sombre that afternoon, I saw tacked to his bulletin board the very clippings I had sent him . . . but they were mounted *with the texts facing the wall!* By some profane coincidence, on the reverse side of almost every clipping was a photograph or rendering of a woman's throat—from swimsuit ads, necklace ads, wine ads. Really, it was unbelievable! It wasn't true of every clipping I sent him, of course. On the back of another was a photo of a pair of surgical gloves. On the back of another were the words THE END. And on the back of another was a likeness of William Shakespeare.

Sadilsa thanked me for the clippings, but said he found the stories far less interesting than the mosaics of the advertisements he had found on the other sides. These, he boasted, had given him an altogether brilliant idea for a most original new film. He explained that there would be no script, that the narrative would be wholly improvised, using only the clippings for structural guidance—particularly the obsessive pictorial recurrence of women's throats.

Q: *You must have been infuriated, to have your plan backfire so badly.*

A: It proved to me, beyond a shadow of a doubt, that Sadilsa had far more influential partners than I in his employ—the forces of darkness, call them what you will. They were the secret of his success, also the secret of his unknowability. My plan backfired horribly, but it was only the first of many such catastrophes throughout the shooting of this film. And not the worst of them. El Sombre had understood all too well what I had tried to do.

Q: *At last:* Throat Sprockets. *The film looks like it was shot in Barcelona and Amsterdam. What else can you tell us about the shooting?*

A: *Throat Sprockets* was in fact filmed sporadically over a period of six weeks in Barcelona, Copenhagen, and Halmstad, Sweden. It had no title until the last day of filming. There was an extremely small crew, consisting of Sadilsa, director and cinematographer; Svea Hellstrom, a combination producer/props person/set designer/script girl; myself, I carried El Sombre's battery pack, lugged cable, did lighting, and also drove everyone from place to place in a rented van; there were also a couple of acolytes, younger than myself—Sadilsa delighted in calling them "Pseudo Jorges," peering at me through his dark glasses as he purred the insult—who performed accessory chores like makeup and catering.

Q: *What about the actors in the film?*

A: Most of the women you see in the film were photographed as they were found, and were not actresses except in the broadest sense. Some of them knew they were being photographed, most did not. No one knew what they were being photographed *for*. Indeed, several of the throats glimpsed in the so-called "travelogue" sequences early in the film are exactly that: footage excerpted from old travelogues, which Sadilsa had enlarged because he wanted to imbue the film with something eternal—like the once-alluring throats of women now dead or in advanced old age. All of the actors seen in the flashbacks during the extended therapy sequence were professionals, with the exception of the psychiatrist, who was played by Svea Hellstrom herself. The psychiatric patient was played by an actress from Stockholm—she needed to be professional because of the extensive text she was required to learn (it was the only scripted portion of the film), and it was my understanding that we left Halmstad without paying any of those people. The Glover, as you must have guessed by now, was played by El Sombre himself.

Q: *Really? Then who photographed those scenes?*

A: I was allowed to photograph those scenes myself.

Q: *And the woman? I mean, the woman in the final scene?*

A: Her name was Sinikka. She was a Norwegian film student with an interest in art direction who joined our troupe in Halmstad. Sadilsa allowed her to work as a so-called "production designer" for the studio sequences, which were filmed either in the office or in Svea's apartment in Barceloneta. We worked side by side for the better part of two weeks, and though we had every reason to speak to one another, we never did. She behaved around me as if she was either intimidated by me or attracted to me, which I suppose made her more both intimidating and attractive to me. Nothing is so attractive as attraction, I remember telling Sadilsa.

Q: *That's a line from* Throat Sprockets, *you know.*

A: Another gripe of mine. Anyway, my feelings—when combined with the fact of our close working relationship, the fact that for some reason not even the simplest greetings were being expressed between us, and the abstract eroticism underlying the footage we were filming—our production schedule proceeded apace with my own emotional implosion, a nervous breakdown. I am absolutely convinced that the film was made for the sole purpose of staging my nervous breakdown.

Q: *What makes you say that?*

A: For some reason I cannot explain—can still not explain—I couldn't bring myself to speak to this woman who aroused so many unmanageable feelings in me, and so I found myself, after a week or so of eating very little and crying myself to sleep at night, having to confide in someone. I didn't understand what I was feeling, you see. It was chemical, physiological, beyond words. Like the cinema. I hoped that perhaps someone like El Sombre could explain.

Q: *So you confided your feelings about Sinikka to* El Sombre?

A: Yes. The second backfire. I was on the verge of implosion; I wasn't thinking. I was having a production meeting with Sadilsa behind closed doors. He saw that I wasn't concentrating fully, that I was *incapable* of concentration. I told him that I had fallen, and so forth. He sat back in his chair and told me that he wasn't surprised, only surprised that it had taken me so long in this crazy business of making motion pictures where you must lead your way with your heart, and he asked who was this lucky girl. At first, I told him I preferred not to say. When I said this, he seemed to recede with disappointment, and even in my state of mind a little voice told me that this just might be it, the shared secrecy that would finally bond us as true friends, true equals.

And so, yes—God forgive me—I spoke Sinikka's name.

El Sombre looked at me without speaking, then he smiled and said that he was impressed, that she was a good choice. I remember telling him that choice had nothing to do with it. He told me that Sinikka was an intelligent girl, very attractive. You may think this peculiar —I certainly do—but I had been too overwhelmed by the effect this girl's mere presence had on me to have considered whether or not she was attractive. To me she was nothing less than a force of nature. Sadilsa took a long, hard look at me, as if he was trying to measure the depth of my torment, and told me something that took my breath away. He confided to me that "Nika" had also worked behind the camera on his last picture and that, during that shoot, he and she had shared a running joke about sneaking away together to some hotel. I smiled weakly; I had won the confidence of the great Sadilsa at last. But my own confession had deflated my spirit, and I felt nothing shift in our mutual imbalance, no sense of victory, still no true friendship.

I was so naive, it took weeks for my brain to bloom with full-blown horror at the disadvantage at which I had placed myself, and poor Sinikka, too, without thinking. And then I realized that he had seen how upset I was, that I was literally combustible with emotion, and hadn't taken me into his confidence at all. In fact, it was obvious to me that his joke about running off to a hotel with Sinikka was nothing of the sort. A horror surfaced into my conscious-

ness, that I may have confessed my love of Sinikka to a
man who was already her lover . . .

And so I withdrew from Sinikka even more, and was
slowly consumed and obliterated by my reluctance. My
reluctance was to get too close to the truths she might
have known, if you understand.

Q: *You were afraid of rejection?*

A: Not at all. I was afraid of *acceptance*. After Sadilsa had
planted his evil seed in my thoughts, I found myself suddenly afraid of how she might make love, that her techniques might be monstrously advanced or perverse or otherwise contrary to the pure and beautiful spirit conveyed
by her face.

Q: *You saw Sinikka as the receptacle of Sadilsa's worst secrets?*

A: There was an interesting tension between us. There were
years between them.

Q: *Backtrack a minute, Jorge. You're describing a crew member, not an*
actress. I was asking about the woman at the end of the film, the one
whom the Glover presents with the—

A: I *know* who you mean. . . .

The morning after my confession to Sadilsa I arrived
on-set at Svea's apartment—feeling vaguely exposed and
deeply vulnerable—to find Sadilsa blocking a sequence
with Sinikka. She was sitting in an antique chair in a low-
cut opaque nightgown with a large volume of Shakespeare
on her lap. She looked absolutely radiant, her beauty pale
and haunted. Her skin was like moonlight on milk. As he
saw me enter the room, El Sombre kissed Sinikka on the
hollow of her shoulder, excused himself with a bow that
made her smile, and approached me. He told me that our
heart-to-heart the night before had given him a wonderful

idea. My infatuation with Sinikka had helped him to see how all of the women we had filmed in the past weeks had borne a vague resemblance to Sinikka—how they had all been dark and sullen—how they had all evinced a certain pale and haunting beauty—and then he announced that Sinikka would appear in front of the camera for the film's final scene, which only I could photograph because I loved her. He added that he had also risen from his dreams with a new title for our film. Yes, at that moment, he called it *"our film. . . ."*

Svea was making coffee in the kitchen as we shot the scene. The only direction I was given was to follow the dictates of my own eye as it responded to the scene. He called "Action!" and we began. And then I saw what you and thousands of others have seen. I expected him to kiss her, to caress her, you know—to humiliate me. Instead, he bit her throat . . . sank his teeth in her . . . and drank her blood. Sinikka didn't react. I imagine that he hypnotized her. Then he produced from his pocket the famous indigo band and fastened it about her throat. I had to look away, but the camera was rolling, so I panned down to the book in her lap. I noticed that Sinikka's blood had flowed onto one of its pages, and a few moments later, my camera ran out of film. What the film didn't capture remains indelible in my memory: Sadilsa rose from her throat, her blood smeared across his mouth, and shouted at me the title of "our" film.

I'm sorry, but I cannot bring myself to say it. . . .

Q: Throat Sprockets. *What happened then? What happened to Sinikka?*

A: I lost consciousness, perhaps from the shock of everything. I awoke a few days later on the couch in the office, which was always unoccupied during the editing of a new film. I tracked El Sombre down at his editing suite. I demanded to see Sinikka or, at the very least, have proof that she was still alive. He told me that Sinikka was gone, that I had waited too long to tell her how I felt . . . that I had lost my only chance . . . and he invited me to watch as he edited the footage I had shot of them together. "It's strange," he told me. "Watching the footage from your perspective I can almost feel everything that you felt for her, and yet I can also see something in her eyes, at the moment my lips touch her throat, as they look back at you. . . ."

He froze it for me on the Steenbeck. It was true. Sinikka's eyes stated plainly that she was waiting for me to declare myself, to object. And I finally understood that there had never been anything between her and Sadilsa, that Sadilsa had simply used her to get even with me for trying to sabotage his career. It was possible that Sinikka had felt something like my own emotions, but had been— like me—too shy to express them, and because of my hesitancy it had been my curse to watch her fall into the hands of a monster.

Q: *When did Svea commit suicide?*

A: During postproduction, shortly after the final assembly. She was present, I understand, at a screening of the final cut, which I did not attend for obvious reasons. It was a couple of years before I found the courage to view the completed film.

The last time I spoke to her, Svea told me that the film was not as effective as they had hoped. The last scene was perfect, she said, but the earlier footage of the other women wasn't as persuasive or indicative or foretelling as it should have been. It needed something more. I suggested that less was more, and consequently Sadilsa began to inflict a series of blunt splices on the film—a leftover technique from *El Sombrero Grasiento,* of course—which was once again very effective. The man knew more about destruction than construction. But this was not the most important of the postproduction alterations.

Q: *What do you mean?*

A: Sadilsa's company, as you know, was a small operation. He supervised every phase of filmmaking from scripting to production, from editing to the production of prints. This is one reason so few prints of his films existed; he was a control freak. During the final days of postproduction Sadilsa left one morning to go to Svea's apartment, and I was asked to mind the office and answer the phone. Everything that could be done to the film had been done; neither Svea nor Sadilsa was a hundred percent pleased with the picture, but they declared it "locked down," ready for printing. I received a call, later that afternoon, from the leading newspaper, requesting Sadilsa's comments on the death of Svea Hellstrom, to which I offered my own comment that there was no truth in the rumor.

His trip to her apartment that morning . . . the discovery of her body that afternoon . . . the small package he was holding when he returned . . . not wishing to be disturbed as he struck the first prints . . . all of

Sadilsa returned soon after, looking his usual self, carrying a small package in his hand. He told me that he was going to strike some prints and didn't wish to be disturbed under any circumstances. I mentioned the call to him, and he said to me, almost incidentally, "Alas, Jorge, it's true. . . . If the press should call again, tell them that Svea Hellstrom was a valued colleague, whose contribution to my current project was invaluable, and that the film's future success will in no small way be hers."

His trip to her apartment that morning . . . the discovery of her body that afternoon . . . the small package he was holding when he returned . . . not wishing to be disturbed as he struck the first prints . . . all of these things coalesced into a new horror when I finally saw the film itself, long after I had seen Sadilsa himself for the last time. You need a certain acuity of vision to discern it—and it is far less noticeable, but nonetheless present, on videotape—but I could see very clearly on the original thirty-five-millimeter prints a reddish tint. I suspect, at the very least, that Sadilsa discovered Svea's body and collected some of her blood before notifying the authorities, then added her "contribution" to the C-22 developer used in striking the relatively few prints that were made. I repeat: That is the *least* I suspect. The *most* I suspect is that Svea's suicide, like all aspects of filmmaking, was a collaborative effort.

Q: *Have you any idea of Sadilsa's current whereabouts?*

A: I've heard that he is directing television commercials somewhere in North America—someplace obvious—under another name. Perhaps it is his real name, for a change.

Q: *Do you have any closing statements, Jorge?*

A: Only this: That anyone who is capable of screwing over a friend is capable of murdering a loved one.

Q: *What are your future plans?*

A: I would like to find a place on earth where they do not yet know the cinema and find better ways to make use of my eyes. Maybe I'll drive a bus. Perhaps when I deserve it, I'll find a good woman—someone like Sinikka, in whose goodness I could believe only after seeing it subjected to the vilest horror. . . . I don't know what I am going to do, really. I suppose I must find some way of rediscovering my faith in people.

• • •

I have been so engrossed in the transcript that I failed to see the end of our campfire coincide with the sunrise. *The roseate tint.* I close the magazine, feeling informed and used and ashamed, and pausing first to stroke the child's sleeping head, I return the magazine to its file cabinet—where other lost souls may come looking for it. I walk with my cane and shoulder bag through the standing portal of the fallen *fachada* to the top of the crumbling stairs, a vantage overlooking the desert valley as sunlight paints its winding dirt roads. I feel magically, expansively aware of the present tense of my own life, for the first time. I see the morning and feel grateful for it, for my presence in it.

The dirt on one of the roads below is in motion. Something down there is kicking up clouds, and the closer it comes, the better I can hear the cantankerous motor propelling it. The child has heard it, too, and almost before I can imagine how I might come to her defense against visiting forces, she is poised at my side with her small arm wrapped protectively around *me.* I cannot help admiring her throat, the small freckle on her rapid pulse that will blossom in her womanhood, and it shames me. The same immensely dilated eyes that found our dinner last night peer across the landscape into that distant dust cloud and relax.

"Is okay," she reassures me. "Is *paisano.*"

But she has spoken too soon. Almost immediately an overwhelming sound of activity reaches our ears from the *other* side of the rubble. She dashes, I hobble, to the view from the rear of the building, where an uneven, grumbling wall of faceless aggression is mobilizing toward us from the line of the horizon. The *cinemateca* is the only possible meeting point between a singular and a mass visitation.

"*Los bomberos,*" she shouts, pulling me back to the other side of the building. The fire men.

Much closer now, we can see at the forefront of the singular dust cloud an old and battered school bus, navigating at pitiful full power the winding road that rises to the foot of the stairs below the *cinemateca*. Its noise is insignificant compared to the roar that is rising behind us.

The bus stops below us, but keeps its engine running. In order to be heard over its noise the driver—swarthy, sweaty, and unshaven—jumps out and shouts up to us from halfway up the stairs, where the crumbling begins:

"*¡Tu allá arriba, vimos el humo de tu fuego! ¡Están acercando! ¡De prisa! ¡Ven con nosotros, quizás es tu última oportunidad!*"

Used to following her instincts and trusting me to follow mine, the girl runs into the driver's arms without a second thought. He picks her up and my eyes fill with tears as my tough little survivalist becomes a child again. He sets her down and pushes her toward the bus, where she is intercepted by two brown-skinned surrogate mothers.

The driver urges me with his hands to follow.

"*¡Baja, viejo!*"

The child looks up at me, encircled by her adoptive family, as if her heart is breaking with our brief bond.

"Don't worry about me, *chiquita*," I tell her. "We'll find each other again. We always do." I wave her on and make my decision known by taking a seat on the steps.

One of the women carries her onto the bus.

"You want to die maybe, *viejo*?" the driver chastises me in broken English.

The child finds a seat on the bus and presses her face and hands to a dusty window. She looks like a face on television, on a movie screen. My face in her eyes, as they urge me to seize this last chance.

"*¿Por qué él está sentando así solamente?*" the driver screams at the child. "*¿Él no sabe que estarán aquí en algunos minutos, para traer este lugar hasta el infierno con ellos?*" In frustration the driver starts to reboard the bus—terrified of whatever forces are hot on his heels—but the women question his surrender.

"*¿Qué pasa?*" they demand.

"*¡Déjale!*" he yells. "*¡Déjale besar el culo del diablo!*"

I watch as the driver releases the vehicle's brake and it rattles away, the face of the dark-haired child who saw me through the night at its receding window, bumping through the winding roads to freedom.

I have nowhere to go. I am where I want to be.

I reach deep inside my shoulder bag and find *The Complete Works of William Shakespeare*, which I reopen to its stained page. The time for requital is now at hand. I read the underlying passage to myself and I can hear, reaching me from a distance of time or space, Sinikka's exact inflections:

If thou and Nature can so gently part,
The stroke of death is as a lover's pinch,
Which hurts, and is desir'd.

I close my eyes, sealing out the clamor and the danger of the landscape of consequences, plotting a return to the original landscape of promise and bliss.

The moment I have waited for has come. I open my mouth and lower my head to the surface of page and type, touching my tongue to the brick-red smutch. Gradually my saliva is absorbed into the page, thirsty with dust, and slowly I can begin to distinguish between the taste of the paper and the flavor the Glover knew shortly after his eyeteeth broke the skin of Sinikka's throat. Tasting her own blood as it reactivates, unwarm but otherwise as present as the day it was spilled, is like stepping through the screen at the old Eros Theater, conveniently suggested by these ruins on the other side of the globe.

Her yield has a tang that flowers in my senses to communicate all that she knew at the moment it flowed: I am overcome with feelings of unspoken love and abandonment, and I have an intuition of danger. I hear the sound of heavy boots coming in strength, scrambling up the hillside behind me. My sense of self-preservation tells me to lift my tongue from the page, to break contact, *run*—but it has taken me so long to come to this, I cannot tear myself away. Images spread from my tongue to my brain. I can sense the Glover behind me . . . he has become real enough to block the sun from my back . . . he winds the choker about my throat in a rapid, soldierly movement . . .

THE END

. . . and, awakening to the empathy that is the belt of indigo between our blue planet and the final darkness, I hear the sound of a garroted camera as my blood runs out of film.